A SHIP CALLED HOPE

Edited by Suzanne Gleaves
and Lael Wertenbaker

A SHIP CALLED
HOPE

by William B. Walsh, M.D.

NEW YORK   E. P. DUTTON & CO., INC.   1964

To my wife Helen and my
three sons without whose
love and understanding
there would be no HOPE.

Foreword

This is the story of HOPE's first trip. It was the maiden voyage of a unique idea. We were a people-to-people mission to heal, and to train men and women in the emerging nations to heal their own. It worked so resoundingly well that we were able to sail again, with confidence and enthusiasm. Now, after our second and third tours in South America, we are preparing to go on to Africa.

During our first adventure, we met with every conceivable frustration and made, I suppose, every possible mistake. It was trial and error all the way, and all the way we grew steadily more efficient and effective.

I have been as frank about our initial shortcomings and the difficulties we surmounted as I have about our successes. We learned from everything that happened, and rarely made the same mistake twice.

HOPE has lived up to its name—that short, bright challenge painted boldly on the side of a white ship. It carries hope to new nations. We teach and we also learn from them.

By doing so, we embody the America we believe in, a peace-loving, friendly nation. The Communists offer the countries we visit "friendship," too. The biggest overt difference between them and us is that we ask nothing in return for what we offer, except friendship.

Our beginnings in Indonesia and Vietnam were dramatic, and the impetus is still felt in the East—as well as sending us on to other continents. Now we know that we must go on, and on; that we are needed and wanted all over the world in the years to come.

WILLIAM B. WALSH, M.D.

Contents

Illustrations

Drs. Ratcliffe and Walsh, President Sukarno
Dr. Benner
Dr. Youker and Technician Phillips
HOPE's gift of milk
The Iron Cow
Fathers Magner and Anna

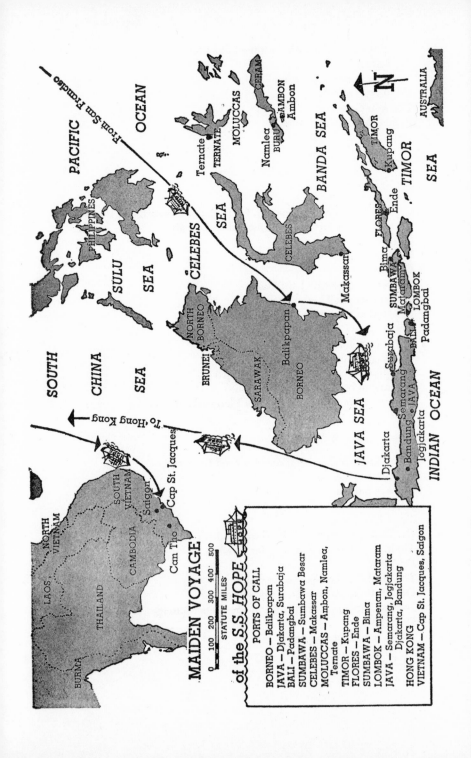

Part I

Hope in the Outer Islands

Chapter I

Project HOPE was my idea. I am too proud of this to be falsely modest about it. Other men may have had similar notions but it occurred to me independently. In bringing the idea into actuality I had the help of thousands, including two Presidents of the United States and the U.S. Navy. Except for the idea, I can claim only a moderate share of the credit, but from the first moment when I thought of such a ship, the *Hope* became my vocation and obsession. I believed in the dream of her even through months when it seemed quite impossible that she should ever sail.

Her story is an American saga. We are known as money-grubbers, capitalists, Yankee barbarians. The power with which we emerged from World War II has been bitterly resented: "Yankee go home." But we have to lead the free world whether we like it or not—or there won't be any. Our government has poured fortunes into foreign aid. The *Hope*, I believe, is a dramatic and effective symbol of the national trait that makes our power bearable. As people, we reach out to other people with the wish to help them when we have little or nothing to gain from it. It astonishes and disarms the people of other nations when they see and understand our crazy personal generosity.

In 1958, Health Opportunity for People Everywhere, its name derived to fit the letters H O P E, was organized. I was its chairman. We were not a government project, though we had a blessing from the White House and were given a disused Navy hospital ship. We were just people ourselves.

Over the next two years we activated and equipped our ship. She was to bring medical help to any country which needed and asked for it. Our mission would be threefold—

to teach, to heal, and to be a pilot for what we hoped would grow into a great white fleet.

Our doctors were volunteers. Nurses and other personnel were paid only token wages. Free enterprise donated our supplies. Countless individuals contributed our operating funds.

From the first, the infinite resources of American generosity were open to us but the obstacles in our way had been very nearly insurmountable. On September 22, 1960, when we finally did sail from San Francisco, it seemed in the nature of a miracle. We were not really ready, but we did not dare delay by so much as another week.

As we headed into the Pacific bound for Indonesia, there were still major problems to be solved among ourselves before we met the problems of dealing with the Indonesians. That maiden voyage was a difficult proving ground for the staff. Our first performance in Indonesia barely skirted the edges of disaster. In Djakarta, Surabaja, and Bali we were feeling our way to an understanding of how we should operate. It took time to learn from our mistakes and our successes.

This will be a false story if I neglect the struggles we had. It will be false if I underestimate or overplay our achievements. As well as a tale of our dramatic adventures, this is intended as an honest report to all those who gave, or will give, money, time, and heart to the *Hope*. Let me tell first, though, about the islands in the Indonesian archipelago where the reality began to approach the dream. Let me begin in Sumbawa where we were blessed by the whole population. There we found Mala, the little hunchback, who became a symbol of Hope. How suitable it was that we reached Sumbawa during the first Christmas season.

Sumbawa Besar was by no means an ideal place for our purposes. A coral reef prevented the ship from coming in alongside the pier. We had to play out our anchors a quarter of a mile offshore. Late December was the season for monsoons and our captain announced flatly that in a storm he would head for the open sea at once.

By this time we had encountered enough suspicion and hostility in Indonesia to be wary. If we were forced to steam away with the ship's hospital full of sick Sumbawans they might think they were being kidnaped by the Yankees, hostages in some dark Imperialist plot.

For the first time we were off the tourist track. No Paul Gauguin had painted Sumbawa and no Somerset Maugham had made its denizens known in the West, and they knew nothing of us. Foreign aid had made no dent in poverty there. A starvation economy precluded the possibility of a decent livelihood for most of the inhabitants. Though the island looked beautiful and lush, malnutrition was common, tuberculosis endemic, and there was no preventive medical program of any kind. Furthermore, in the harbor sunken hulks reminded us that the last mission to this port had not been merciful.

HOPE's medical men were worried most on two counts. Would the people here trust us enough to be treated at all and what about our mission to teach and learn? There were only two local doctors for 250,000 western islanders. One of them was a man brought in under government contract. The word "contract" conjured up mechanical and indifferent practice. The other was a young Chinese recently graduated from college. Could we demonstrate American techniques to these two? Could they share with us their special knowledge?

We were shorthanded ourselves. I had not taken into account the effect of holidays on our schedule. Many of the rotating medical specialists who flew out to join us for short periods of time chose other dates. There were only seventeen physicians aboard, including several Indonesian volunteers traveling with us from Djakarta. Normally we carried twenty-five American doctors.

Our nursing and sustaining staff members were less nervous than our doctors. They had all signed up for a year and, for the first time since we had set sail four months earlier, felt wholly optimistic. Though troubles surmounted, they had grown confident. The Indonesian nurses taken aboard in Djakarta for training were now trustworthy teammates. Core and backbone and heart of the project, our women were the first to cast off all doubts about our mission.

Under tropical December skies the water in the crescent-

shaped harbor did not look treacherous. *Hope* launches pulled
away and headed toward a jetty built expressly for the arrival
of the ship. On the jetty a crowd stood waving. "Well, it's
the friendliest beachhead America's made in fifteen years,"
commented Tim Lally, the radiologist.

He, nine other doctors and technicians, chief nurse Claire
O'Neil, chief operating nurse Mavis Pate, and chief medical
secretary Johana Vettoretti landed first. Stepping out of the
crowd, Dr. Poch, Sumbawa Besar's contract doctor, greeted
them. His lined face told of overwork and of too much
care for his patients, not too little. There were tears in his
eyes.

In a short, graceful speech Dr. Poch welcomed the *Hope*
on behalf of himself, his Chinese colleague, the islanders, and
the local chief, Bupati Kepala Dearah. By recommending that
we come, the Department of Kesehatan (Health) in Djakarta, he said, had made the Sumbawans feel important and
happy.

Our two jeeps were brought ashore from the launches and
our advance contingent drove seven miles into the town of
Besar. All along the route freshly painted signs proclaimed us
allies in fighting a common enemy, disease.

The small procession of vehicles drew up in front of a
palace once inhabited by a local maharajah. "Palace" is a
term used in the islands for any big house built for a big boss.
This one was one of solid masonry with a portico over a
broad flight of tiled steps leading up to the main entrance.
We had already learned that Indonesians like any excuse for
ceremony. To commemorate this occasion, they posed on the
steps with us for the usual smiling photograph and then we
and they exchanged flowery speeches. Beneath their formal
words we heard a desperate cry for help, and we responded.

When the handsome doors opened and we walked in, we
were shocked speechless. The palace was a pesthouse.

Small bamboo mats carpeted the floors wall to wall. On
them lay the blind, the crippled, the disfigured, the con-
genitally abnormal, people with yaws, people with horrifying
skin ailments that bled and suppurated, people with monstrous
growths. The tubercular coughed and spat indiscriminately

among the uninfected. Beside the patients squatted relatives, ready to bring water or to cook rice on little primitive stoves. They expected to feed their own; Indonesians are family people.

Room after room had been stripped of furniture and converted to this emergency use. Men, women, and children had been gathering for days and weeks to wait for us. From the mountainous back country they had come on foot, in springless carts or by ancient bus, for a rendevous with HOPE. The challenge was enough to make merciful men despair.

Alexander Sahagian-Edwards, M.D., of the Francis Delafield Hospital staff in New York, took a shallow breath in the fetid air, stepped forward, and put himself brusquely in charge. The small, dark American of Armenian descent had tireless energy and the habit of command. He ordered each corner of each room cleared, the patients moved somehow, and tables set up. Every table became a diagnostic center.

Ambulatory patients immediately dragged themselves into long lines and mothers and fathers queued up with their sick children. Dr. Poch helped to sort them into categories of ailments.

At one table Mavis Pate from Texas, handsome, calm, and imperturbable, scheduled the operations our surgeons would perform in the next few days. Beside her, tidy, delicate, New York-born Johana Vettoretti registered names and diagnoses. The process was handicapped by linguistic complications. Sumbawan dialect bore little relationship to Indonesian. Local interpreters aided those from Djakarta to translate Sumbawan into Indonesian into English and back again.

The girls worked at a killing pace, pausing only to smile at the children. Mavis thought Mala Kuzuma, clutching his father's hand, looked like a child-sized version of the Hunchback of Notre Dame and she gave him a special smile.

Mala did not smile back. His expression had settled into that of a suffering old man. With his disfiguring hump, he had been too long a figure of fun to accept any smile at its friendly value. To her great relief, since such conditions are often incurable, California's Dr. Paul Spangler told Mavis he thought Mala might be helped. Mala's father understood no English but he knew when the nurse put a band around his son's wrist that he was chosen for treatment. So did the boy. Looking up at Mavis, Mala's face gradually broke into a slow, hopeful grin.

As soon as the sorting of cases was well under way, Alex called a senior conference. The ship was a long way out in the water. We should treat most patients on land if we were to make any headway in the impossible case load. A task force went to investigate the town's three hospitals, but they had a total of only 150 beds, all full, and no operating rooms. Scattered in the uplands of the Sumbawa Besar region were seven polyclinics administered only by practical nurses. Surgical cases would have to be handled on board the *Hope*. A message was sent to activate the third of our three adult wards. As for the rest, we would need a shore clinic beside the harbor and some place nearer than the palace in Besar for applicants to come.

With the enthusiastic cooperation of the local authorities, a dirt-floored customs shed in the harbor area was cleared to serve as a clinical base. Five tables went into it, four for examinations and one for the pharmacist. A field tent was set up as a laboratory where simple tests—urinalysis, blood pressure, and the like—could be made. Canvas mats and a tarpaulin propped as a lean-to would keep the murderous sun from those who had to wait. Our invaluable handyman, Leo Haney, probably the one irreplaceable member among us, started constructing an incinerator.

There was no running water dockside, no electricity, and no toilet facilities. Water could be brought from the ship in barrels and hurricane lamps would do for light, but it took one of our prettiest Indonesian nurses to solve the last problem. Though the Indonesians thought us prim. we were not prepared to take to the bushes. She used her blandishments on a group of dock workers and the men erected a rough cylindrical object out of corrugated iron with an entrance facing modestly seaward. It served the purpose, though to avoid being baked by the heat inside no one stayed in it for long. Almost at once it began to list, settling gently into the sand on one side. Before sundown we had nicknamed it our Leaning Tower of Pisa.

By five o'clock that first day hundreds of people had been diagnosed and fifty of the gravest cases, mostly surgical, transferred to the *Hope*, Mala among them.

The *Hope* was ready for them. All the work that had gone into making a peacetime hospital out of an over-age Navy vessel, all the trouble we had been through in the United States and in Indonesia, all the efforts to make a group gathered from every state in the union into a functioning unit that could meet these and any other conditions, seemed in that moment worthwhile. Ten *Hopes* side by side could scarcely alleviate the misery on this green island in the Flores Sea, but one was a miracle in itself. You begin where you can and do what you may.

Those Sumbawans who were brought aboard had never before been separated from their families. Most of them had never seen beds, much less slept in them. They took to the showers like all Indonesians, who adore water, especially running water, but several climbed in with their clothes on before we could stop them. We had already learned to limit shower time to ten minutes. Our first patients in Djakarta had stayed an hour unless forcibly removed.

To explain things we had commandeered two local translators. Even so, since our Indonesian nurses did not yet know all our ways, misunderstandings were as inevitable as they were good-humored. Pajamas proved a puzzlement. Sumbawa is pantless. Several patients solved the problem by wrapping the bottom halves around their middles. "Sarong?" inquired one man politely. Another who couldn't figure out the use of a washcloth rolled it into a tiny turban and put it on his head.

There were a few nervous complaints from the patients as they were settled into the wards, but most of them made it easy for us by being so submissive, willing, and stoic.

Mala Kuzuma was given a pair of blue pajamas and a pair of white slippers and taken into the nursery. Gloria Aguilera, nurse-volunteer from Pueblo, Colorado, who was to care for him during most of his coming long ordeal, tucked him into bed between fresh white sheets. He did not smile again, but there was satisfaction written on his face.

We had watched him enjoying the ride in the jeep, the trip across the bay, standing in line to have his blood sample taken, giving information to the interpreter for the printed form a secretary filled in to cover his case. He was twelve years old and born in Besar.

As the last launch pulled away from the jetty, Sahagian-Edwards looked back at the hastily built lean-to, the bulky customs shed, and the intoxicated-looking cylinder we had christened the Leaning Tower of Pisa. Everything was in readiness for the morning and almost everyone had gone home. One man stood alone silhouetted against the island's shore. Mala's father was still staring out to sea after his son. Across the water the great ship stood out against the crimson tropical sunset like a huge white bird. The letters H O P E, fifteen feet high, painted on her side were visible until the sun sank and darkness descended. Then you could see only the blaze of her purposeful lights.

Chapter II

Mala was born robust and happy-natured. His parents had great plans for this, their first son. He would be sent to the Islamic school in Sumbawa and if he turned out as bright as he was beautiful might win a scholarship to the Islamic University in Djakarta. As he grew in grace Mala's only flaw was a little bump the size of a marble on his back. His mother thought it would disappear. Instead it developed until by the time he was five his small shirt bulged with it. When he entered school the other children pointed and laughed at him. Indonesian youngsters may have a special sweetness but they can be as cruel as any others toward the grotesque. Mala rose straight to the head of his class but he developed a deep, impenetrable melancholy which worried his teachers and his family.

His father took him to the best hospital in Besar, a rambling low structure with a faded title roof. The Indonesian doctor there, sole practitioner in the region at the time, told Mr. Kuzuma that nothing could be done unless he sent the boy to a big city. For a man supporting thirteen people on his bank clerk's salary, such a thing was out of the question. When Mala was ten years old, Dr. Poch arrived. He was a highly trained German physician, but he could not help Mala either. "Your only hope is in Djakarta or Surabaja," he told the Kuzumas.

Writing to the governor was a last and feeble hope. Sumbawa had thousands of ill people waiting for a share of the governor's limited funds to help them. Two years later the Kuzumas learned that a hospital ship from America was due to reach Sumbawa in Demember. After that, Kuzuma told surgeon Paul Spangler, "We devoured every bit of news we could get about this ship and we watched its progress eastward from Java with hungry hearts. For months we have prayed and prayed to Allah that our son would be accepted as a patient."

This man's prayer was answered, but what of other prayers?

Instead of sending Hope, some say, we should have established an American hospital in Indonesia. Yes, but where? On Sumbawa—or on Bali or Flores? In Lombok or Semarang?

We wanted to accomplish many things. We hoped to demonstrate how medical practice works in the average hospitals of our republic and we deliberately limited ourselves to techniques readily adaptable to local use. We wanted to teach, to hand on knowledge, and to learn for ourselves about them and from them. We wanted to make friends for the United States and hoped that our voyage here would cause ripples of good will to spread throughout troubled eastern waters.

During our brief stay in the harbor at Besar we were able to treat over 700 sick Sumbawans besides Mala. Grateful patients are any doctor's greatest asset and these were a national asset to the U.S.A. Together with their relatives in such a close-knit family society, our friends on the island surely still number in the thousands.

Besides that, whatever else we could not leave behind in a place where there was so much need and so few professionals, we could and did change the image of America and Americans. Until *Hope* came into her bay, Sumbawa Besar knew America only through Hollywood. Townsfolk saw Elvis Presley and Elizabeth Taylor in the movies. They knew about cowboys and millionaires and gangsters. If they reached high school, the children were taught English (sketchily) and something of our politics, picking up a good deal of miscellaneous information, some of it accurate. "Your President Kennedy is four-four years old," one boy solemnly informed Alex Sahagian-Edwards. But outside of such tidbits the islanders knew little of us and had never seen plain Americans in the flesh.

They were curious enough but their curiosity mingled awe with antagonism. Although Communist propaganda had been less effective in western Sumbawa than elsewhere, American propaganda had not reached them at all.

The Sumbawans do not readily trust any strangers. Islam is the local religion. Many women wear heavy veils and bodies are seldom exposed. The sight of some of us, men and women, in Bermuda shorts shocked them at first. Women doctors and nurses were phenomena. Except for midwives, the medical profession in their limited experience was almost exclusively male. Only the people as ill as Mala or as desperate as his father were willing to take a chance on us before we arrived. The others came only to look and see.

What they saw they trusted. In the makeshift lean-to by the sea, twenty waited for us the first morning, sixty on the second. By the third, one secretary's list already ran to twelve typewritten pages, single-spaced. Alex asked Dr. Poch to help screen out the hypochondriacal and the incurable.

Some curable diseases had gone too far to treat. Diabetes was rampant and the nearest large supply of insulin was in Djakarta. We blessed the pharmaceutical houses back home which had donated quantities of the drug but we knew the relief we brought was temporary. Perhaps the government could follow up our efforts and send more insulin according to the need we uncovered and reported. Tuberculosis, too, needed a long-term effort to wipe it out. We could and did, though, set up a mass X-ray clinic to screen out those with active TB and we lectured on the danger of infection. In a campaign to protect the schoolchildren, we checked as many as 200 schoolteachers in one day.

We did what we could, and to everyone we offered at least kindness, vitamin pills—and milk. A truly inspired feature of the ship was her Iron Cow, a mechanical marvel that parlayed sea water and powder into fresh, rich milk. Gallons of salt sea went in; gallons, quarts, and pints of milk came out in containers on which were emblazoned the crossed flags of Indonesia and the United States. HOPE was printed on one side; HARAPAN, "hope" in Indonesian, on the other. The word may not have carried exactly the same connotation in Sumbawan but they understood the substance. Children were urged to gulp it down as fast as we gave it out and their elders fondled the cartons they carried away.

Our popularity burgeoned daily. We were determined that at least we would clear Dr. Poch's insane case load and give him and his colleague a fresh start. To handle the rush, Alex went from ship to shore many times a day, seeing to it that chaos did not develop under pressure. He was a patient man with the sick, especially with sick childern, but not at all so otherwise. The slightest delay in procedure made him wild.

By now the islanders would give us anything, do anything for us, but one day Alex found them too slow-moving. He had missed the launch and refused to wait for the next trip. Instead of bothering to negotiate through two interpreters for a canoe, he headed for one on the beach, climbed in, and shoved off. Its rightful owner began to yell. Alex paid no attention until he realized that this proprietary alarm was not for the craft but for the foreign doctor. Under Alex, the canoe began slowly but surely to sink.

While the launch wheeled to the rescue a crowd gathered on the jetty calling advice and encouragment. As Alex settled deeper into the water, he snatched off his stethoscope and unstrapped his camera, holding them both high over his head. The sea closed over man and objects just as the launch came near. When Alex bobbed to the surface he saw a nurse on deck with her camera pointed at him. "Stop that," he ordered impatiently, "and throw me a line!"

The long trip by launch out to sea gave us some powerful advantages. We had a chance to develop unity as a working group, order as a hospital. Before this we had functioned under conditions more suitable for a circus. In Java and Bali, where we were anchored close to shore, we had been engulfed by friendly visitors. To cranky air conditioning, sudden leaks, and other special and unaccustomed hazards, was added an almost insuperable traffic problem. Corridors were jammed and wards so filled with interested spectators that nurses had to run interference for each other to get through to patients. Our big classroom with its closed-circuit TV overflowed and the top medical men who wanted to watch our surgeons at work crowded into the three small operating rooms. We wanted as many of them as possible—every lesson we taught, every demonstration, was a permanent legacy to Indonesia—but their presence made difficulties.

In Sumbawa we could concentrate on the sick. We didn't use our TV classroom, but our complement of Indonesian nurses was getting intensive instruction on the run. They had to run to keep up with our girls.

All together, eighty-eight operations were performed, taking from minutes to more than six hours. The fifty-five major surgical cases required elaborate post-operative care. What impressed the Indonesians most was the amount of personal attention given to each one. Chief nurse Claire O'Neil, quick-humored and big-hearted, was a great believer in TLC (tender loving care) as an aid to healing. It is part of our tradition.

We Americans learned, too. There were problems never seen at home. Perhaps the great difference between conditions in America and those in Indonesia from a surgeon's point of view lay in the size growths attained unchecked. Nothing had been done because there was no one to do it.

A comparatively young woman came aboard in a chair, her

abdomen so swollen that she could neither lie down nor stand up. She had been thus burdened for over five years.

Mavis Pate had difficulty positioning her on the table for Dr. Norton Benner, from San Mateo, California, to remove what proved to be a benign ovarian tumor. There was only one basin big enough to hold the specimen and we put it away to take back as a medical curiosity. The woman lost a third of her weight when it was gone.

After carrying so much ballast for so long, she had also lost all sense of normal equilibrium. At first her nurse tried to teach her to walk again by holding onto a bed or rolling table but such a counterbalance was insufficient. To over-correct this woman's posture, the nurses devised an un-orthodox but effective treatment. Her wrists were tied together behind her knees and from this arbitrary crouch she gradually straightened up. When she was discharged she seemed only slightly tipsy as she walked, unaided, down the gangway. In a few weeks she would be able to toe a straight line or carry a basket on her head along with her naturally well-balanced countrywomen.

Modern surgical cures often seem like miracles and surgery is always the most dramatic form of medicine. Even minor surgery can remake human lives.

Many of those born with cleft lips in Indonesia spend their whole lives horribly disfigured. This repair, long since taken for granted in the West, was reserved for the rich or the big city dwellers. One Sumbawan women who came to us with the skin drawn up under her nose, exposing her teeth, told Mavis Pate she had been married only a year. "At last," she said to Bob Pulliam joyfully afterward, "my husband will not mind looking me in the face."

Nothing, though, is quite so dramatic a gift to a human being as his sight. From the time the *Hope* landed in Djakarta I had worried because there might be no ophthalmologist aboard for Sumbawa. Where doctors are scarce, cataracts grow unchecked. God was good. In Bali Dr. Diehm, a highly trained German eye specialist, offered to join us until we could pick up a rotator from home.

Among those who waited for him in Besar's palace pesthouse was a family of four. Not one of them had more than two-per-cent vision left. Hand in hand they had stumbled many miles to reach the port city. They were led aboard the *Hope* by a nurse, still holding to each other. When they left they held their heads high and stepped in single file down the gangplank. The most hard-boiled of the staff and toughest members of the crew were touched by the wonder of it.

And then, of course, there were the children. Indonesian children are a combination of spunk and gentleness, patience and deviltry, bright eyes in brown bodies. It is heartbreaking to see so many of them disfigured by skin diseases, suffering from curable congenital abnormalities, crippled by infectious ailments akin to polio.

Sue Glocke had charge of the post-operative care of six small orthopedic patients. A girl with expressive, caterpillar eyebrows and no fear of strange languages, Sue paraded her hobblers up and down a walkway with railings rigged on the side. "*Djalan! Ber-jalan! Walk! Walk!*" exhorted Sue. Claire, watching the show, nicknamed her "my sister Eileen." Before we left, those children debarked from the launch and merrily formed a conga line on the jetty, chanting "Walk! Walk!"

More than any other child, though, somehow young Mala became for us the personification of all Indonesia's hurt children, their needs, and what we could do for them. Perhaps it was because he had carried his burden and his melancholy to the threshold of young manhood and because he was so grave and yet so quickly responsive to his experience with us.

He showed his delight with rare smiles of great sweetness and he began at once to learn English and to communicate with us in order to show a greater politeness. He had never heard of air conditioning and found the nursery a little chilly at times, but he did not say so. He was amazed and pleased when a nurse brought him an extra blanket and thanked her extravagantly. And thank you, he added, for the nice pictures, making a wide gesture to include the whole parade of cheerful circus animals one of the nurses had painted on the walls.

On the morning when he was waked early and prepared for his operation he showed no signs of alarm. "I was really not afraid," he said afterward, "because I knew that these people were my friends. I only thought how lucky I was."

Examination had not revealed whether Mala's tumor was a simple lipoma or a mass with spinal chord involvement. Mala was lucky. Dr. Spangler probed and found the growth deep-seated and widespread but it was lipoma and could be removed. After two hours Mala was wheeled into the special ward for post-operative patients and woke to find Gloria Aguilera looking down at him. "How do you feel?" she asked, familiar with the misery he must be undergoing. "Just fine, thank you," Mala said.

He never complained of his pain and intense discomfort. When his back was probed he managed to keep quiet by biting his lip and when each ordeal was over he smiled.

The HOPE surgeons all gathered around his bed each time his dressings were changed. Afterward they held conferences out of his hearing. The skin flaps would not take hold and grow together. We would have to try elaborate grafts. Time was short and if we had to leave Mala behind we might well have only made things worse for him.

Chapter III

We had to prepare to go on to our next port. The last patients scheduled to come aboard were those needing only minimal post-operative care. Weariness made the staff long for a day at sea even though the next stop was in the Celebes where, according to rumor, doctors were a popular prey for professional kidnapers, worth, it was said, 10,000 rupiahs apiece—alive.

Even enslaved captives, one man said, could scarcely be asked to work any harder in a given amount of time. This was no complaint but a boast and a way of expressing satisfaction with what we had accomplished. Just one patient's story was enough to account for high morale.

This man, a middle-aged farmer, had come in to us from

the hills. A widower, he lived alone with his young son, and the two of them scrabbled a bare living from three acres of poor soil. Each year they ate half the crop and sold the rest.

During the last few years his long hours of work had tired the man unbearably and he was never free from pain in his chest. Even on his rare visits the itinerant doctor did not stop to see him. Others were sicker. He worried constantly about what would happen to his boy if he could work no longer.

News came, by wind and by rumor and at last by official bulletin to his tiny village 140 kilometers inland, that a medical ship was coming from America. The village chieftain assembled his people and read them the bulletin. He told them anyone who wanted to could go for treatment. The farmer gave in his name.

Round-trip fare by bus was 100 rupiahs, $2 at the official exchange, ten per cent of his annual income. When the time came, he paid the sum and set out with thirty-five others for the maharajah's palace in Besar. There he waited three days, sleeping on his mat, eating rationed rice. Fear claimed him. It was a myth. He had spent a fortune for nothing. Such a ship would never come. If it did he heard whispers that it would be a charnal house.

When the jeeps rolled up to the steps he knew we were real. The farmer got a band for his wrist right after Mala did. Arriving on the jetty to board the launch, he said to an interpreter, "Now I can see I have nothing to fear. The ship is beautiful. I am happy because I will be well."

His chest tumor was encapsulated and could be easily removed. He was a strong man and recovered very quickly after the operation. Before he left us, he asked the interpreter to explain what we meant to him. At the end he added, "Tell the Americans this very carefully. In former times I had to give five kilos of rice to foreign officials who came to my village. The Japanese sent them over and over for the rice and when they came my son and I afterward went hungry. This is the first time in my memory, or the memory of the oldest man in my village, that foreigners have come and not taken rice from us. You are here to help us. We will not forget. We will never forget."

These words echoed a refrain we heard over and over. They meant to us that we had accomplished at least part of our purpose. If it saddened us to know that we had not been able to help all of them, it was heartwarming to find that what we could do aroused such profound gratitude. The *Hope* to these people was a miracle, a gift from heaven by way of America. Even the hopelessly ill appreciated our kindness, vitamin pills, and milk. They would not forget us, nor we them.

Alex's formal report to the U.S. on Sumbawa ended:

> In sum, two weeks of extremely active operations were carried out. All acute problems in this period were managed by the HOPE personnel, and all diagnostic and problems of a chronic nature received consultation and medication. It was felt that the latter was a major contribution in easing the load of the resident physician in Sumbawa. In addition, large supplies of drugs and equipment were left for his use.
>
> A tremendous amount of good will was established as evidenced by the demonstrations of the native population and the consensus of the HOPE medical personnel was that the Sumbawan operation was highly successful and rewarding.

But that was not quite all. At a meeting the medical staff discussed the case of Mala. We had no authorization to take an inpatient with us. It looked now as if Mala would need additional plastic surgery much too finicky for the local doctor in a hospital where there was grave risk of infection. Besides, he should have therapy to straighten his spine after his wound healed. It was decided to request special permission to keep him on board a while longer.

Before we left, the Sumbawans wanted to do something to show their appreciation. Being very short of worldly goods they planned an entertainment for us. On the last Sunday the water buffaloes were all rounded up from nearby fields for a race in a rice paddy.

As head nurse, Claire O'Neil was guest of honor, seated in the front row of a grandstand behind a bamboo railing hung with rattan fringe. The HOPE guests came and went as the sun climbed high, relieving each other from duty.

The show began with a parade under flags in butterfly colors, some printed with flowers. Topknots of fresh flowers

adorned the animals and looked like little Easter hats between their horns. For the races each driver drove his lumber-
ing team so that the yoke passed over a stake with a buffalo
on either side of it, an intricate maneuver. The field was
partially dry, partially flooded, and the races were run splash-
ing down its length in a long series of heats.

"It was quite a sensation," Claire wrote back home, "to
see those great animals come charging straight at you. There
were moments when I would have been happier to be less
honored—in the back row. All the same it was a grand party."

To top the party, we had a cable from the Indonesian HOPE
committee granting permission for Mala to travel with us, if
we had his family's consent.

Mr. Kuzuma listened carefully when we explained to him
that we needed time, but that even with time we could not
say for certain that we could cure his son. If we took Mala
along, we could not bring or send him back to this island until
April, when we would land in Bima, on the other side of
Sumbawa, a very great distance from Besar. Would he trust
us?

Mala's father did not hesitate. "Please. I will come to Bima
for my son. This treatment may mean a whole new life for
him. I will do anything you say. My wife does not fear, either.
I am only so happy I cannot express it to you in words."

With that settled, everyone aboard felt better.

No Christmas mail, or any mail, caught up with us in Sumbawa. When New Year's Eve came we celebrated with a
dinner party but very few had the energy to see the New
Year in. A long way from our "home" base in Djakarta, we
felt very isolated at holiday time. Nevertheless there was real
holiday spirit in the wardrooms and tiny cabins and even in
the crew's quarters. The crew was thankful because the ship
was leaving this primitive island and looked forward to being
in a city. The staff just felt good.

The night before *Hope* sailed a small number of visitors
came aboard. Among them was a short man in a black petji
followed by his mild-mannered wife in her best robe. Two
children and three men in black petjis followed them. As
they entered the post-operative ward, the man introduced

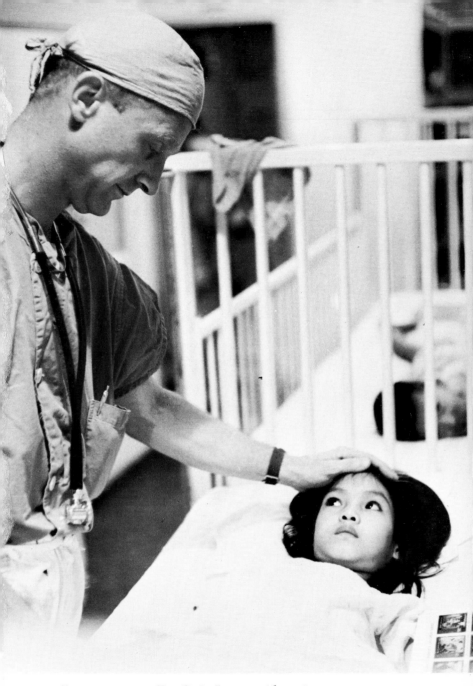

Person-to-person. Dr. Craig Leman with patient

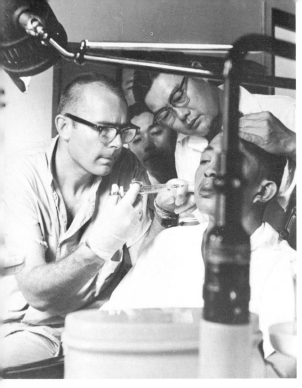

Teaching was HOPE's prime objective. Oral Surgeon Philip Fleuchaus demonstrates injection

Nurse Gloria Aguilera instructs Indonesian student nurses in ward procedures

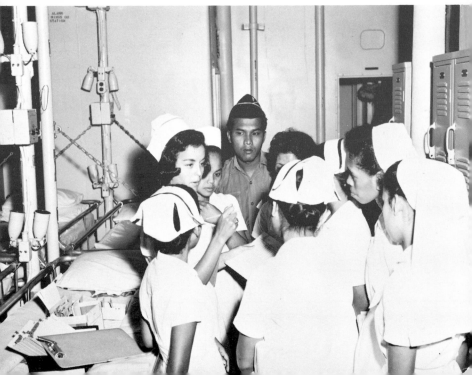

Richard Neal, medical technician, works with university student Suharta in ship's laboratory

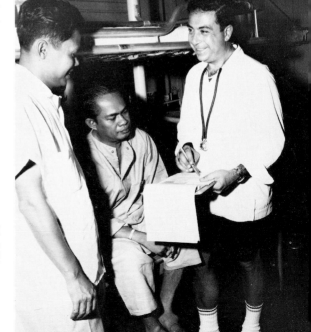

Indonesian colleague and patient listen to Dr. Sahagian-Edwards' summary of a case

We are welcomed at the Rajah's former palace. Inside, it was a pesthouse

Midwife Harriet Jordan and her Indonesian counterpart interview patients. Children look on

himself to Gloria Aguilera. "I am Mala's father. This is my wife and these are two more of our children. Also here is my wife's brother, my son Mala's schoolteacher, and a friend of ours who drives a car for the government office."

Mala set up in bed, grinning. On display he had laid out the puzzles, books, and crayons his American friends had brought to him.

"He is so excited about going with you," Mala's father said to Gloria. "All his life he has told me, 'Someday I want to go to America.' Now he will be in a little bit of America for three months."

Before the last good-by Mr. Kuzuma slipped a small roll of soiled bank notes into Mala's hand. Leaning over the bed he said softly, "I have saved this for you. It is 400 rupiahs. Use it wisely on your voyage. Do not forget what you have learned in school and remember to pray to Allah every day. And we will pray to him for you and for these people."

During shipboard services our chaplains, Father Magner, the huge red-headed priest who had spent many years in China, and the Episcopal Reverend William Anna from Maryland, also offered special prayers for the Moslem boy.

In Makassar, our next stop, we needed all the prayerful intercession possible, both for the *Hope* and for Mala.

Chapter IV

When I had been there, in Makassar, the year before on my survey trip, I was grimly advised that the five miles between the airport and the capital of the Celebes Islands could not be traversed after sundown. In the dark hours farmers along the route left their plows and took up guns.

This rebellion was religious and led by fanatics. Sukarno had insisted on a unified country and the militant Islams in the Celebes wanted their faith to become the state religion now that the Dutch were gone. Using this martial creed as cover, anti-Sukarno elements of various kinds joined the rebellion and bandits used Islam's star as an excuse for profitable lawlessness.

No one knew quite what to expect as the *Hope* steamed toward its next goal, but morale was high. Sumbawa had given us unity and the feeling of achievement. Minor irritations had vanished.

The air conditioning was still erratic and when it worked sounded like an old-fashioned runaway express train. The ship's swimming pool had long since sprung a leak, our dozen movies had already been exhausted, and the limited library of books had been read ragged. If the girls were annoyed because the promised "beauty shop" turned out to be in charge of a crew member who gave choppy haircuts and didn't know a pin curl from a rolltop desk, they no longer mentioned it. Betty Ahern, R.N., from Fond du Lac, Wisconsin, trimmed and pinned anyone who asked her. As for personal laundry, one washing machine and one dryer could be reached only through a female W.C. An elaborate schedule was set up to avoid unfortunate encounters and men and women cheerfully took turns catching up with the wash on the free day between islands.

And Mala, on this one free day, had a procession of visitors. I suppose we were superstitious about Mala as well as deeply concerned for him as a human being and our patient. His case had been accepted as risky, but the risk had become a personal matter to everyone. If we could not heal him, we would feel a disproportionate sense of failure for which any number of successes could scarcely compensate. I don't suppose there was a single member of the staff who did not make whatever contribution he or she could to this one case. The next two weeks were crucial ones in Mala's prognosis.

Meantime we had to face unknown and possibly hostile conditions in Makassar. Die-hards and bandits had retreated to the hills and the government was theoretically in control; at first our reception seemed royal and as if we were welcomed as friends.

The afternoon we arrived the entire ship's complement was

entertained by the governor in his handsome palace on the outskirts of town. Some seventy-five local dignitaries ranged themselves around the marble-floored ballroom and we circled under the huge chandelier, conscientiously shaking hands.

Orange crush was poured (no alcoholic beverages, naturally) and entertainment provided. Tom-tom players squatted in a corner accompanying a group of ten-year-old girls dressed in sunshine yellow with fireman's red tops and plaid sarongs who danced with a fluttering of fans. The chief of police performed on a bamboo instrument, his sentimental repertoire including "Whispering Love" and "True Love." Six older girls danced at the last with ethereal grace and charm, their hands incessantly in motion.

On the wall a seven-foot portrait of Sultan Hasanuddin, hero of the Celebes, looked benignly down at us. He was the equivalent of our George Washington and the city's medical school as well as other institutions, streets, avenues, and parks were named for him. We liked his face.

We were also welcomed by fifty local doctors, about a dozen of them Europeans. Ostensibly they were happy to have us. Actually they wanted either to use us for their own purposes or to make monkeys of us.

If we were, as they claimed to believe, a collection of superspecialists they would take credit for having brought us there. As a challenge to our mythical skills, they had a hundred impossible cases waiting for us. In one instance we were asked to replace an arm with a new live one—or, if this was beyond us, to provide an artificial limb at once: this is a part of the world where standard treatment for compound fracture was amputation.

Actually, without the specialists who would arrive after the holiday hiatus, their collective skills were greater than ours. Makassar had an astronomical ratio of doctors to population compared with Bali and Sumbawa. The Hasanuddin hospital had excellent modern equipment and beds with clean sheets. Makassar's medical fraternity was immediately aware of the position we were in. Waiting to see how we would handle ourselves, they watched us during the first day's screening of the patients they had lined up for us.

Our surgeons found only eight cases that could possibly
be operated on and then only after putting the patients in
condition. The medical men came up with only half a dozen
more.

Our whole visit might have been a fiasco. Besides the
medical dilemma, it rained that entire first week. Moss carpeted the whitewashed walls of houses. When the rain let
up for ten minutes and the sun blazed in the suddenly blue
sky, everyone raced for windows and doors and portholes
to take a deep breath of fresh air before sheets of water
descended again. Technician Mary Jo Ann Crary wrote back
to Utah, "I have come to believe that part of the essence
of Indonesia is gooey, black, sticky, plain old MUD. It oozes
over the soles of your shoes, it catches at the wheels when
you ride, it bogs down buses, harbors the hookworm and who
knows what else?"

Considering the situation, we refused to be downed. For
the three weeks we were there we decided to concentrate on
seminars, lectures, and nurse-training. We were not trying to
compete but to help.

Instead of trying to cram the ship with patients, we opened
her to visitors. Tied up to the dock, we held more fascination
than any American movie, even in Cinemascope or Tech-
nicolor. Eight thousand people, not counting cases we did
take aboard or personal guests, came to see the *Hope.*

Outwardly she had no special features to distinguish her
from any medium-sized ocean-going passenger vessel except
the size of her name on her white flanks. Once across the
deck and in the interior, wardrooms, dining salon, and small
staterooms were civilian and ordinary enough, but every other
inch of her non-engineering space was working hospital. The
large auditorium with ranks of classroom chairs, with writing
arms, had three TV screens high on the walls. Doctors scheduled most of their instructive surgery in No. 1 operating
room in order to use the closed-circuit TV, and an intercom
system made it possible for the audience to ask questions
while procedures were under way. Outside, in the lobby,
were scrub sinks, and the nearest unit was for Intensive Care,
a new concept to most of our medical visitors.

We had everything a small, shore hospital has routinely: laboratories, medical library, physiotherapy room, dental clinic with three chairs and shining equipment, central supply, X-ray department, anesthesia room, eye-ear-nose-and-throat clinic, GU department, hospital kitchen—all ordinary except that every movable object was capable of being secured. That niggling job had to be done every time we put to sea.

No frills or furbelows intruded on the severity of the metal bulkheads, no cruise ship "extras" existed. Cabins were remarkable only for their smallness. A very few were singles, more doubles, but the majority were for three or four. Space was at a premium and the room where the nurses changed into non-conductive shoes to enter the operating area was the size of a closet. An inventive crew member had peeled a log, split it, and inserted pegs for hanging up outer garments. The sight of wood among so much metal was soothing to the spirit.

Down below, our Iron Cow was a maze of machinery almost as formidable as that which ran the ship. It was also equally noisy.

Every part of the Hope was noisy. Air conditioning saved our lives and impressed our visitors, but it roared constantly in our ears. We had to raise our voices and speak over it as if everyone were deaf.

Our 8,000 visitors were fascinated to see where we lived and worked. How American and efficient it was, they said over and over.

By the time we reached Makassar, some of the plainness had been alleviated. Our people had rapidly developed a taste for Oriental art. Posters and water colors and oils of island scenes were attached to the walls of cabins and in the gangways. The visitors appreciated this, too. Just from looking, they began to understand the friendliness of our mission. When they did, they responded.

Lecturing at the Hasanuddin University Medical School, Drs. Beaubien, Hanan, Elliott, and Wier were overcome when not only the medical students but the whole undergraduate body showed up to hear them. From the School for Assistant Pharmacists in Makassar 120 students came to observe the

ship's pharmacy, and two English-speaking Indonesian professionals from the TB hospital and the public hospital volunteered to assist in the pharmacy the whole time we were there.
When they weren't dispensing drugs beside Charles Dickerson
and Fred McKinney, those two studied in our library, eagerly
devouring books on their subject.

Four of HOPE's American nurses were asked to aid in the
surgical ward at the county hospital, Rumak Sakit Unum.
Dorothy Aeschliman told us that the eighty-seven-bed ward
had only one thermometer, five syringes, and five needles.
Regulations called for 9 A.M. injections. After lecturing for
four days on everything from neurology care to communicable
diseases, Dorothy worked up a talk on daily routine. Instead
of such a lunatic timetable, she suggested a relay system to
allow for five injections every hour. The instruments could be
then properly sterilized in between.

"It may not sound dramatic to Americans," commented
Ruth Currie, R.N., "but we also showed the hospital staff
how to use ambulatory patients for making bandages, folding
bags, and other useful work as well as getting them up and
around. Those patients had been staying in bed all day with
nothing to do. We got them out on the porch and encour-
aged them to read and talk together as well as working on
such projects. The best bandage maker turned out to be a
one-armed man who had been classified as useless."

Physical therapy was practically unknown, although the
hospital did have one licensed therapist who came to call on
Sue Glocke. She asked him how many patients he worked
with in a day. "None," he admitted. He had no room assigned
to him so he filled in his time acting as a nurse. "As if," said
Sue furiously, "therapy needs a separate room!"

It wasn't the standards of effective medical procedure so
much as peripheral conditions that needed improvement in
that city. Fifty Makassar nurses were added to our traveling
Indonesian group for three weeks of instruction while we
were in port. Before they left, our nurses drew up an instruction booklet which the Makassar contingent translated
into the local language.

Ashore, HOPE's sanitary engineer worked with health officials on tests of the water supply and consultations were held on prevention of epidemics. Milk flowed daily into the town from our Iron Cow 8,000 pounds of powdered milk were offloaded for distribution throughout the southern Celebes.

In Makassar's pediatric hospital wards exceptional attention was given to separating out contagious diseases; a high standard of care prevailed and Donald Duck and Mickey Mouse danced on the walls to cheer young patients. But it was heartbreaking to find so many youngsters there because of complications caused by malnutrition. "The children," nurse Ann Roden observed sorrowfully, "often resemble the little pigeons they serve you at Chinese restaurants."

One looked like a tiny monkey, the mechanical kind that climbs up strings. "Drs. Elliott and Wier brought him in," wrote Sue Glocke. "The first and perhaps the last myositis ossificans any of us had ever seen. He is cute, about three years old, already half petrified, with restricted movements of his arms, though he can still talk.

"They also brought us a dwarf," she went on, "an eleven-year-old who looks about four. I would swear he was a miniature Buddhist monk. He does not smile and stays in whatever position you put him in, just staring. I sat him on a bed cross-legged, his arms in front of him, and there he still may be."

Though we took only a limited number of adult patients on board in Makassar, the pediatrics ward was full. Next to Mala we put fourteen-year-old Ishak. Mala offered chief pediatric nurse Mary Finley paper and crayons for Ishak, who drew the *Hope*, which he had glimpsed only briefly as he was carried on board. Dick Elliott was so impressed he dug out a book on perspective from among his possessions. Ishak studied it avidly and soon incorporated the principles in his sketches. Father Magner, who often took the boy strolling, swears we have started a distinguished future artist on his career.

The supply of toys was already low. We never refused children who wanted to carry favorites home with them. Just as Mary Finley was beginning to worry about it, a seaman appeared at the door of the ward with an armload of new ones. "I have no idea where he got them," she said. "But it

was great. He brought enough for a couple of ports." She
herself raided the bookshops in Makassar for stories her
patients could read aloud to each other.

Sue Glocke, working with handicapped youngsters, had
one girl in her teens who was deaf and dumb. For three
hours a day she coaxed the child to speak. The youngster's
mother pled with her to try hard for the kind foreign lady,
and at last a ghastly rumble issued from the girl's lips. It
was the first sound she had made in twelve years. Sue tried
to get her to transform these grunts into simple syllables but
was stymied by the guttural pitch of her voice. All of us
shared our problems by now, and Sue consulted Johana, a
choir soloist at home. Johana drew a ladder. Each time the
girl made a sound, Sue walked her fingers up the ladder. The
croak began to climb. After a week she could manage comprehensible two-syllable words and furthermore an Indonesian
medical student from the university of Makassar had been
trained to continue her treatment. It would not end when
we left.

Good will began to mushroom toward us. Our rotating eye
specialist, Dr. Paul Tisher who flew in from Connecticut, was
asked to work with Makassar doctors at the outpatient clinic
of the public hospital. Our surgeons were welcomed in all
the hospitals and Dr. Walter Haynes, fresh from Columbus,
Ohio, performed the first open chest surgery ever seen in the
Celebes.

Professional meetings were held Mondays and Fridays
aboard the *Hope*, and our staff and the local men prepared
papers for each other. The exchange worked well. "A great
deal of thought went into the presentations," reported Marion
Wier, "and they were successful."

American dental supremacy was never challenged, there or
anywhere. Makassar dentists were happy to consult ours and
brought patients aboard the *Hope* for special work. Our
dental team also judged a "good teeth contest" for the local
Dental Health Program and donated a doctor's kit as first
prize.

Besides this, we began to be deluged with invitations to

visit homes, meet people, join in excursions. The gangplank ran two ways.

When we went off to see the mountains or to picnic at the foot of thundering waterfalls, we were taken in a convoy, led by a truck on which swiveled a loaded bazooka. It still wasn't safe to get very far out of town. Also it rained. Riding in buses with wooden seats, wearing sneakers and raincoats, we were treated like royalty and like royalty we needed iron bottoms, twelve-hour kidneys, and a royal indifference to danger and discomfort.

It was worth it. When the road ran along the sea, fragile Makassar schooners dotted the coves and the horizon with green, pink, and black sails. All over the landscape small potbellied children who wore nothing but a string and a charm sat on water buffaloes and fished for minnows. Dwarf palm leaves thatched native huts, and Maripa palm, coco palm, sugar palm, fan palm, date palm, rattan or climbing palm, and sago palm grew in green rustling groves. Banyan trees put down their myriad roots from great gray branches and tree ferns spread upward toward the sky, thick and lacy. It was as beautiful as a dream of visiting the tropics.

We were also fascinated with lives lived so differently from ours. At a wedding we watched a girl of sixteen as she sat on a bed under a tent made of fine white organdy looped up with silver ribbons. The groom, a college student and quite westernized in other ways, arrived in a long red coat worked all over with silver flowers. On his head was an elaborate arabesque of silver topped with a pink rose to match the rose in his lapel. Attendants carried a gauzy red canopy over him.

The groom sat down on the floor of the girl's bedroom with the elders of both families around him and did all the consenting. After the questions were asked, the most important elder grabbed his hand and asked the important ones over again. He could, they said, feel it in the groom's hand if he was not sincere. Indonesians use handshaking for both courtesy and pledge.

Elder satisfied, ritual concluded, the groom was permitted

to sit on the bed with his bride while the wedding party gathered around. With bridesmaids and bride in yellow and orange and groomsmen in red, it was extremely picturesque and not at all like a wedding at home.

Nor was nurse Nan Campion's visit to a rajah like visiting anyone in the U.S. "Our oldest patient, who had recently been discharged, picked me up in his car one afternoon when I was walking around shopping. When he invited me to his house all I could think of was *The King and I* and of course I accepted. The Rajah was about eighty-six years old and the wife who had visited him in the hospital was about forty, but when I got there he took me into a bedroom to see six wicker cradles containing six recent babies, all his. Four generations lived under that roof and I met about thirty people, all part of the family.

"In the courtyard women were weaving sarongs. It takes three months to make one and these were astonishingly beautiful, some with gold threads, some with silver.

"In the parlor, which ran the whole length of the palace, there was a trophy case filled with spears and krises, and for my benefit the Rajah put on his fanciest sarong and took out a kris to show me his quick draw.

"When I asked for a picture, all his wives and lady relatives lined up with him. Every face was happy. It made me realize how different they were. In the U.S. all those women would never be happy living together and sharing one man."

One of the Indonesian nurses, Miss Zahariah, explained to Nan how such a household works. "You can tell where papa is going to stay at night," she said, "by which door he puts his shoes outside."

Person to person, with mutual tolerance, people to people, we won friendship and success in Makassar in spite of the obstacles that met us on our arrival. Before we departed thousands of people who had not been able to get aboard the ship gathered at the pier entrance, pushed their way past the guards, and finally broke the police lines. When they found it was impossible to get up the gangplank they yielded good-naturedly and cheered us over and over. On the ship we were crowded with mementos of their friendships. Each nurse had a present from the medical fraternity which had met us at first with closed faces and distrust. Carved birds and alligators and beautifully made models of Celebes houses and jewelry of the fine white gold for which the area is known had been given us as tokens of esteem.

We also carried a new patron saint. At his farewell party for us the governor had ordered the portrait of Hasanuddin taken down from his palace wall. The enormous painting was a national treasure. It was presented to the *Hope* as a gift. This legendary hero of the islands was installed in a place of honor in our classroom.

All during the three weeks in port, we aspirated serous fluids from Mala's deep wound and gradually the skin flaps had begun to heal. As he got better, his melancholy disappeared, and a chipper and delightful spirit emerged. He engaged our affections ever more deeply and we took special pride in his improvement, in the now very nearly certain prognosis that we would return to Sumbawa with a healthy, unhandicapped boy.

And as water widened between us and the Makassar dock, friends were shouting good-byes and promising to write. Our gratification was great, but the pleasure we took in it was mitigated by a tragedy which had brought death to the *Hope*.

Among our seamen, boatswain John O'Meara from San Francisco had made as many friends as the nurses did. Instead of yielding to the temptations a big city offers sailors, or yielding to boredom when we stayed in primitive places, John was always off hunting with the islanders. Hunters are an international brotherhood and communicate easily in a common language, ignoring the confusion of tongues. An optimistic, cheerful man, unhappily John was also careless. On every table aboard the *Hope* bottles of aralen, protection against malaria, stood beside the salt. We were warned to take it regularly. John did not bother and one day while he was hunting in the mountains near Makassar an infectious mosquito bit him. Within hours he had a fulminating case of malaria which caused his circulatory system to collapse. We were helpless to save him and when he died flew our flag at half-mast.

After we left Makassar Father Magner read the Mass for the Dead and in the presence of us all consigned John's body to the Bandac Sea.

Chapter V

Timor, where we landed next, is very poor. Here Communism's pie-in-the-sky promises had attracted many converts and quasi-converts. In a frenzy of fear that HOPE might make allies for the U.S., the Timor Communist Party had put on a blanket anti-HOPE campaign. Widely distributed circulars, printed in red, described our mission as a medical calamity. According to the propaganda, half the people we treated had died. Furthermore, the Communists claimed that a *real* hospital ship was on its way from Red China and wise Indonesians, they said, would wait for it. "Everyone knew" that Americans hated all people of color and merely used them as medical guinea pigs.

Even the Timor medical profession was confused about us and the populace was actively antagonistic. Before we landed local authorities uncovered a serious plot to blow up the HOPE. Orders from Djakarta grounded the Garuda Airlines plane scheduled to land on Timor and our rotating doctors were kept out of the area while paratroopers flew in to round up the ringleaders of the plot.

These men were not agents of the Internationale, but Timorans who had believed the lies about us. Indonesian army officers arrested them and when we came into port brought them aboard the ship to see for themselves.

It took just one tour to convert the local revolutionaries. They saw everything, from classroom to Iron Cow, met Mala, talked to him, to the staff, to the nurses, and poked about in labs and special units. Afterward not only did they apologize; overcome with remorse and shame, they offered us the use of the Kupang Communist meeting hall for our clinic!

We accepted. On its walls hung handmade posters condemning the *Hope* and the U.S.A. Photographs of Mao Tsetung glowered at us from all sides. All this we ignored, and after we had been there a day or two, patients began to turn up in droves. Sometime or other the photographs and posters were taken down—but not by us.

We made no overt propaganda. Ours was a privately sponsored effort and we believed that medicine should know no politics. Communists were treated when they asked to be, exactly the same as anyone else.

To help us with the problems of local customs, including touchiness about color, our remarkable Ambassador had suggested I accept the services of a USIS man who knew the languages and the people well. I agreed that to have him with us would be a fine idea and Ted Ashford was detached from duty to go along with HOPE. A Negro incidentally and an able foreign service man, Ted was an immense help. Medicine came first, but we were discovering how many other things counted as well.

The first Sunday in Kupang, while the islanders were still making up their minds about us, a few of the less timorous Timorans invited Norton Benner and several of the girls to play tennis in town. The sets were relaxed, easygoing, and fun. Someone suggested that it would be a good idea to have a ship-*vs.*-shore basketball match. We thought so, too.

Movies and books are beyond the means of most people in Kupang. Sports are their major entertainment. They were, as we were to find out, exceptionally good at games.

From among our staff we managed to collect a scratch team. Most of them had not played since high school and none of them had ever played together. Nonetheless they volunteered for the sake of international friendship.

It was quite a show. To our amazement, at least 500 spectators gathered at the field. Her Excellency, the wife of the governor of Timor, tossed out the first ball. Our "first" team dauntlessly shook hands with the referee, glanced dubiously at their trim opponents—and bounded awkwardly out to do the best they could.

Everyone from the *Hope* who happened to be off duty was

there to cheer. Mala, well enough to make his first trip to shore, sat in the front row rooting irrepressibly for his American friends. But no cheers could save us and Mala spent most of his time between cheers rocking his head in his hands to express his chagrin as the score piled up against us.

The Indonesians were lithe, fast, and great basket shooters. Our men missed easy shots, dropped the ball at crucial moments, and when they passed it was all too frequently to their adversaries. As Dr. Kuharic, internist from Seattle and captain of the HOPE team said simply, "We got clobbered."

Mercifully the final score has been forgotten. It was some consolation to discover that we were clobbered by the Indonesian team already selected to compete in the East Asia games. What was good about it was that the Indonesians loved us for going down to such spectacular defeat.

After that we kept right on losing at Friendly Games of basketball, volleyball, and baseball. But not as overwhelmingly as on that first day. We didn't mind losing in a good cause, but we had our pride. Kuharic got better and better with practice and we found out that we had a ringer on the staff: Dick Neal, a Negro who ran the blood bank and transfusion services, had earned an athletic scholarship at Lewis and Clark College. He was in trim and he was tops. From then on I'm afraid we managed to insist that he turn the blood bank over to his assistants whenever we were competing in sports.

Beside our willingness to accept sporting challenges, we swam, skin-dived, sang, and danced with the Indonesians to our mutual pleasure. We felt that this reflected true, basic American attitudes far better than medical aloofness would have done. The one folder we gave out in English and Indonesian stated only that we had been sent by the American people and ended "The American people wish you well." We were American people—"hard-boiled" and practical, but also friendly dreamers hoping for a better and friendlier world.

Occasionally, of course, we were fooled by our responsiveness to any appeal for aid. Take the SOS from Ende. Would we change our schedule and come quick? A volcano had erupted on Flores Island and the town of Ende needed help.

We went, at the price of delay. Ende was a disaster area all right, but not from the sudden upheaval of its volcanic earth or the spewing of its volcano. Disaster was endemic. When newly appointed senior medical officer Dick Elliott, chief surgeon Paul Spangler, and sanitary engineer Richard Marks went ashore to gauge the situation they were met at the high matchwood pier by what looked like at least half of the 3,000 people who lived on Flores. Among them was their one doctor, thirty-three-year-old Lien Gwan Hok.

He cheerfully admitted that the tremors had not multiplied. The hospital walls were torn like cloth, but few patients had been injured. What he wanted was for us to put in a day helping him with his backlog. Elliott, Spangler, and Mark were taken, in spite of their annoyed protests, to see his clinic. Patients sat waiting as if they had been there for all eternity. On their sad faces was written deep, "Allah wills it." Well, we were there, and Lord knows they needed us, even if a special emergency did not exist. What could we do but the best we could?

Eleven doctors and eight nurses were brought ashore. The two-way radio and round-trip launches worked without stopping. Drugs, vitamins, supplies, and milk were unloaded.

Crowds pressed close around the clinic blocking off any air that might have reached our sweltering staff members. Sweat soaked the girls' cotton uniforms. Doctors tied handkerchiefs around their foreheads to protect their eyes from spurting sweat. As the heat grew still more intolerable, a loudspeaker blared instructions and the decibels rose intolerably. Nevertheless more than 500 patients were treated by five o'clock when we called a halt.

At this moment the mayor of Ende proposed a Friendly Game of basketball. The doctors had collapsed, but laboratory technicians and ship's officers made up a team. Play they did, to packed bleachers, and duly lost.

"Hop-ay! Hop-ay! Hop-ay!" chanted the mob that attended our departure from the dock. The fragile pier reeled under festoons of urchins, and those who could not scrimmage a way onto the pier swung from its underpinnings. The slender bamboo structure shook. Cheers rang through the evening air.

As the last launch pulled out, the Floreans started to sing en masse.

Hope weighed anchor at a quarter to eight, her lights blazing against a black night. Across the cove we saw the quiet glow of the no longer active volcano. From the point of view of permanent accomplishment, Ende may have been a waste of time, but we had made another islandful of friends.

Whatever else we did or did not accomplish, everywhere we made friends. "You have brought a little bit of America to us here," said one visitor to the ship from the town of Ambon, where we had been before Ende, "and we will never forget you."

Our specialists demonstrated their modern American techniques all over the islands, but, in the end, it is the simplest lessons that do the most good and for which I suspect we will be remembered longest.

For instance, two of our staff were American nurse-midwives. They worked with female *dukuns* who deliver most of Indonesia's babies. With due respect for island folkways, dirt and superstition were costly in human lives. Wherever Belle Chaffin and Harriet Jordan went, riding in trucks, jeeps, and pony carts over miserable roads to reach the far villages, the *dukuns* noticed that the Americans were always washing their hands If they put across just this one point, the results will be incalculable. Everywhere our women left behind them not only example and precept, but gifts of soap and copies of a manual on obstetrics they had prepared for *dukuns*, translated into the predominant local dialect. "There is so much infant tetanus," said Harriet Jordan with a sigh. "Many of the old women *dukuns* can't read or write so classes are slow. We have to repeat everything and teach by rote. But small changes, like sterilizing knives and washing hands, will save so many babies."

Nurse-training was another major contribution. The Javanese who had been with with us since Djakarta were so well along by the time we reached Kupang that they held their own classes, supplementing those we held.

When they first joined us, the Indonesian trainees had been

inclined to shrug their shoulders and say, "Well, of course, you can do wonders with all the equipment you have." Since November, Claire along with Fran Harris and the others had dinned it into them that if you know what you want to accomplish you can usually improvise with what you have. Our girls themeslves had learned how true this was on the voyage and in the islands. When Claire heard an Indonesian nurse inform one of her countrywomen, "If you understand the principle, you don't need special equipment," she cheered.

We would be remembered in many places for many things.

In Ambon, which was the Royal Dutch Navy base during the years of Netherlands control over the archipelago, the colonial Dutch had no policy for educating an eager and industrious people. Freedom caught the Ambonese very short of trained men. Struggling to meet their responsibilities, the Ambonese welcomed us with open arms.

Because of HOPE's visit, Ambon's water supply is being purified. Working with the authorities, Dick Mark discovered that they were under the impression that a 3/10 of 1 per cent mixture which contained some chlorine was a 3/10 of 1 per cent solution. Better chlorination will bring the bacteria count down from between 10,000 and 14,500 to the desirable maximum of 1,000.

Radiologist Lally completed a mass X-ray survey of 2,500 people in Ambon which showed, unexpectedly, that only five to ten per cent had active TB. The doctors were able to clear their wards of those with other diseases closely resembling TB which could be differentiated only by X ray.

We established the first blood bank on the island, too, as we did in many places over the island nation. It is against Islamic religious custom to give blood and we had to overcome this prejudice. Our staff members gave their own blood—and the Indonesians almost always followed suit. If we could open our veins for them, they would open theirs for each other.

No, they won't forget us however short our visits were. In Kupang, I am told, they still use two dates to reckon time. They say: "Before the Japanese invasion," and "Since the *Hope* came."

I don't know quite what impression of America we left in Kupang, but it was as favorable as it may have been inaccurate in detail.

For one thing, Mala, who now acted as self-appointed liaison officer in the children's ward, assured all comers that America was a land of miracles, milk, sweets, and cinema. To prove his points, he described himself as he had been, exaggerating in a manner worthy of Lon Chaney, and afterward led the ambulant to the canteen for his favorite refreshments, Coke and ice cream. Having attended our movies every Wednesday and Saturday night, he described them at length to the other patients, especially his favorites, *Funny Face* and *Dog of Flanders*. As a mimic he was wonderful. His peers were impressed.

Ashore, Malcolm McCannel was our Danny Kaye. Chased after by myriad children whenever he appeared in the streets, this opthalmologist from Minnesota minced, danced, or goose-stepped along at the head of his dragon's tail of young, teaching them to yell: "Yeah, Minneapolis!" Many a moppet on Timor has the impression that the United States is part of Minneapolis.

To their elders Minneapolis became the symbol of light. Curable blindness shut off the sun from so many in Indonesia. In Kupang, even with two eye specialists along we could not keep up with the cases. McCannel was driven to the decision of Solomon. With time running out, he removed only one cataract per patient, demonstrating the operation each time to a local man. After we were gone he hoped the second eyes would be cleared. It wasn't the ideal solution, but at least he offered each of them one window on the world.

"I think if you take the cataract out of grandma's eye," he said, "it's a lot better than giving her country a Sherman tank. Her eight children and eight grandchildren and all the people they know will be grateful because some Americans made the old lady see. Anyway, who really needs a Sherman tank?"

Chapter VI

We did not want ours to be a crash program. We wanted to leave behind more than vitamins, milk, drugs, medical books, and a record of patients treated. (These totaled 3,500 in twenty days in Ambon and an unrecorded number because we lost track in Kupang where our 8:30 A.M. clinic was described by McCannel as "a pleasant but congested madhouse with every patient accompanied by four or five relatives all wearing wide grins.") I repeat myself, perhaps, but it was vitally important that we also left there, in the hands of doctors, nurses, dentists, medical technicians, students, all the know-how we could pass on.

Among the unnecessary island killers were stones in prostates and bladders. Local doctors had been making abdominal incisions to get at them, a practice which the elderly could seldom tolerate. Our men taught the physicians they worked with how to remove stones without making incisions.

For diabetes we left insulin and also tried to teach the principles of diet. One of Dr. Kuharic's diabetic patients was doing well for a while and then her blood sugar began to rise shockingly. He discovered that her husband was bringing her fruit which cost very little in that land. Kuharic explained that fruit was bad for her. Her husband asked if she could have eggs and was told yes. "All right," he said determinedly. "I will save all my money and bring her eggs. I do love her very much."

In one place Arnold Smoller found a crippling prevalence of an eye ailment due to vitamin A deficiency. It was readily curable by a simple operation, but the local surgeons were much too busy with waiting lists of patients who had more serious needs. Smoller demonstrated the operation to a general practitioner. Together they performed the second operation and Dr. Liang alone, with Smoller watching, did the third. And so it went. They say the East never forgets a teacher.

They say they will never forget us. Certainly while we were there they did everything they could to show appreciation.

When it came time for us to leave Kupang we were unable to go. Several of our generators had been sent to Singapore for repairs and the others, under strain from the extra load, showed signs of imminent collapse. Furthermore, a concrete pipe conducting water into the cooling system was eroding out.

Light and air supplies were endangered. Everyone on board was reduced to taking showers the "Navy way." (Get wet, close the taps, soap, open taps briefly, and rinse.) At the same time communication slowed down. A plane crash on Garuda Airlines grounded every plane. The wireless radio systems were much less efficient than jungle telegraph via hilltop drums. To get messages back and forth, we funneled them through Washington, where I happened to be at the moment. I went into action, Washington to Djakarta, Djakarta to Washington, Washington to Kupang, capital of Timor.

Somehow the American President Line got our generators out of Singapore by freighter as far as Djakarta. Our American Ambassador, the invaluable Mr. Howard P. Jones, offered us the use of the Embassy's own DC-3 to take them on. Piloted by an old friend, Colonel McCartney, the plane brought the heavy generators to Timor, along with rotating doctors who were waiting in Djakarta. That much weight meant no mail or new movies—and no bags of cement to repair the pipe. We needed twenty-five bags, and there was none on Timor.

When our need was known, grateful patients went to the governor. They knew he was planning to build a porch on his house, one that would not rot in the rains or tempt the termites. To achieve this, he had been gradually accumulating a private hoard of cement in bags. The minute he knew of our plight, he donated the whole lot to us. The governor in Kupang would be without a new porch for at least another two years—but, to Mala's open chagrin, we were now ready to sail on for western Sumbawa where his father was coming to pick him up.

What a credit to us this traveling patient, this symbol of our efforts, this very nice boy was. From being inward, sad, and brooding, he had become the most outgoing and liveliest of youngsters. Everyone on board was his personal friend. The crew outfitted him, donating a wardrobe of western clothes from the ship's Slop Shop. Those he didn't wear, he hung in a display around his bunk. He had grown two inches at least and had fleshed out on the milk which he loved provided it had chocolate flavoring or was loaded with "susu." Ann Roden, a favorite of his, never handed him a glass of milk without the sugar bowl in her other hand.

As his English grew fluent and comprehensible, he worked as our volunteer messenger, running errands for the wards, admitting office, and labs. His special pride was to act as Father Magner's personal adjutant and he was often seen trotting beside the huge, red-headed priest. When we were in port, he not only performed as liaison with the other children, but often pushed one end of the stretchers when they were rolled toward the operating rooms.

Straight now as an arrow, he was also a walking advertisement for American dentistry. Dr. Stanley Hellman had done a miraculous job on his very bad teeth.

It's hard for us to imagine what decent teeth mean to an Indonesian. Especially on islands like Timor, their teeth are healthy and strong to start with, possibly because mothers nurse their babies for years. (This, alas, eventually contributes to gallstones.) The food is coarse, good for teeth, and betel nuts, the chewing gum of the Orient, keep them clean even though turning them red. They didn't seem to mind them red. In some sophisticated Asian cities, as a matter of fact, members of the older generation still lacquer their teeth to make them anything but white. Dogs have white teeth. (Beauty wasn't the why of betel nuts, though. One of our staff members tried chewing them and said he got quite a jag on.) But in spite of breast feeding and betel nuts, the diet is so deficient in many aspects that the average adolescent's teeth were already in hopelessly poor shape. And dentists are even rarer than doctors. Wherever we were, mass extractions rivaled X rays in number. Our dentists taught, too, but I think their chief memories are of extracted teeth speckling the islands as the islands speckled the sea.

Perhaps it was partly because he was so pleased with his teeth that Mala smiled so much. Whatever the reason, every time he smiled we were reminded of our success in these strange places and in his smile was thanks from all the people we had come to help and had helped.

To our mutual relief, when we reached Bima Sumbawa, we found a message that Mala's father would not get there until just before we left. He could stay with us until then, and on his home island he was more than ever king of the children's ward and inestimably helpful.

Western Sumbawa presented the same dramatic challenge as eastern. They had just one doctor for a quarter of a million people. In Bima 1,500 patients waited for us, lounging or squatting in the courtyard of an abandoned schoolhouse.

We went at once into high operating gear, in spite of doubtful generators on board and no electricity or running water on shore.

Each morning the green and white *Hope* launch left the ship with medical supplies and a seventeen-man clinic team. Thirty-five minutes later they carried their equipment through the throng, colorful in Moslem caps and orange, green, pink, and purple plaid sarongs. An ice chest of refrigerated drugs went into the corner of the pharmacy. Each doctor took his black bag into his own booth. Administrative records were put onto a front desk and medicines, powdered milk, drugs, and other supplies for the day went on a folding table in the rear of the reception room. A case of cartons of pure water and a short-range radio transmitter and receiver were set up on the back porch.

"We had plenty of improvising to do," said Mary Jo Ann Crary, who operated the lab. "We used direct sunlight for our microscopes but sometimes seven or eight rows of children blocked the light from the windows, following every move with their big brown eyes. If you said 'Shoo!' they melted away, but two minutes later, back they were. We had to get a battle lantern to see by."

Our one-time Communist schoolhouse had the usual photographs of Mao Tse-tung on its cracked and peeling whitewashed walls. No one seemed to notice them enough even to remove them. What Mao looked down upon was unpaid doctors and underpaid nurses working their heads off. In a nearby meeting hall the girls screened patients hour after hour, sweat soaking their cotton uniforms. In our dental clinic, once used by the comrades for a garage, two long benches, one for each of our dentists, were always full. The one local dentist, wife of the only doctor, was busy having a baby so our Stanleys, Hellman and Mayall, had the town's teeth to themselves.

One morning a man was in Hellman's chair while twenty more, hunched on the bench, looked on. In the middle of an extraction the patient blacked out. An assistant ran for a stretcher. He and Hellman rolled him onto it, covered his face with a handkerchief, and carried him outside to recover consciousness. The observers concluded that he was dead and stole away. When Stan came back, the waiting bench was empty. He went fishing that afternoon and caught, to his astonishment and momentary dismay, a shark. The next morning his clinic was as crowded as ever.

We found tuberculosis rampant on the western island. Eighty per cent of those who turned up for X rays were infected. They lived jammed together in bamboo huts that made pestholes of their settlements. We treated them, and provided for follow-up care. Blindness ran TB a close second, and head and neck tumors were prevalent, as well as cleft palates. These fell to Dr. Robert Pulliam, surgeon from Longview, Washington. "I've seen more cleft palates than a busy man sees in the U.S. in a year," he said, meaning he had repaired that number. His theory was that they came from living in compounds, which encourages inbreeding. "The girls don't travel far before they get married."

Pulliam had joined us in Ambon. The morning he arrived he was in the operating room scrubbing up before he unpacked. From then on we claimed he never stopped at all. An extra ward had to be opened to take care of his cases.

A kindly, charming man, tall, shambling, and blue-eyed, Bob was a Pied Piper with children. One of the nurses said going into a town with him was like getting trapped at a Roy Rogers movie on Saturday afternoon. Pulliam, who loves children as they love him, said, "Well, if war can be prevented I'd like to do my share. I don't want my kids ever to have to fight these kids."

He treated his patients of all ages as he did the children. Having grown up in Macon, Georgia, he had the South in his mouth and even years of practicing in the Northwest hadn't affected his Macon American. His Indonesian had the same magnolia flavor.

"Treasure," he said to a young woman named Sei of obviously Dutch extraction, with her light complexion and pale hair, from whose face hung a tumor as large as her head, "I'm goin' to have you lookin' like the Marilyn *Mun*-roe of Bima. Baw-goosey!" Baw-goosey was the Pulliam rendition of *bagus*, the Indonesian word for splendid, fine.

Twenty-five-year-old Sei spoke no English but she understood him even though her face was too pushed aside to permit her any expression. Mavis Pate asked Sei if she would submit to before-and-after photography, which she consented to do. Three days after the 6¼-pound parotoid tumor, well encapsulated, was excised, Sei twitched both sides of her face in an effort to smile for Dr. Pulliam and the camera. With her shorn head and reshaped face, she looked about eleven and a little bit like Marilyn Monroe.

Bob's long and difficult procedures often continued after sundown. Hospital attendants held flashlights while he cleared away grotesque abnormalities and rebuilt human faces. Leaning close he talked to one boy while he performed a biopsy on his salivary gland under local anesthetic.

"*Sakit*? Pain?" he asked.

"*Tidak*. No," replied the child.

"Baw-goosey," said Pulliam. "I hope it's *tidak* all the way."

Baw-goosey became a HOPE byword and certainly affected the language in Bima. Another small boy came up to a HOPE nurse and announced, "President John F. Kennedy is baw-goosey."

The people of Bima were outstandingly trusting and friendly. They made us feel a bit like a company of saints and it was almost disconcerting to have medical omnipotence ascribed to us and taken for granted.

Take the day when Bernard J. Goiney, a Navy surgeon in World War II, was confronted by a Chinese woman with a facial tic. Consultation suggested a resection of the facial nerve, but Goiney was dubious. On rare occasions in Seattle he had used hypnosis in cases like her and he said rashly, "It's obviously psychosomatic. I'll hypnotize her right out of it."

It seemed a good idea when he spoke but then he remembered the language barrier. His Indonesian and American audience took him up at once. He felt committed. Nervously he instructed an interpreter. The interpreter instructed the woman. Within sixty seconds she was out like a light. Goiney sweated. He knew nothing at all of this stranger's problems, of her life. Somehow he kept talking, repeating at intervals, "When you wake up you won't have a tic."

Then he snapped her out of the light trance. Her tic was gone. Goiney took a deep, incredulous breath, squared his shoulders, and waited for congratulations. His American confreres were warm in their praise and astonishment. The Indonesians drifted away without comment. As far as they were concerned, he had said he would cure her and he had. This was merely what they expected.

It seemed to us suitable that our "very own" Mala was a Sumbawan. The whole island had adopted us as their friends as we had adopted him. Though Bima was crowded and poor, her beaches were glorious and we were urged to enjoy them. On Sundays after church; dugout canoes showed up in shoals to take out anyone who wanted to go for a ride. This in spite of the fact that Indonesians really hate to have Westerners in their canoes which sit so low in the water that your hand can rest on the gunwhales while you trail your fingers in the water. They are excessively tippy and our quick, impromptu movements often threatened to swamp them. On our part, we learned to be still and love gliding swiftly over the crystal sea.

We could wander at will as far as we wished, protected by their friendliness. One afternoon Marion Wier was strolling far outside of Bima when it began to pour with the suddenness we never got used to. Running toward a village, she was met

by the local schoolteacher who took her in and arranged to
dry her clothes. A small crowd gathered at once and Marion
chatted with them over tea about children in Indonesia and
in America, leaping the language barrier with signs, until
the sky was wiped clear. Meetings like this, such simple
touching of hands and discussion of universal topics, would
never be forgotten by either side. On cool evenings this
friendly lady doctor took to rambling down the beaches and
then sitting down somewhere to "eat peanuts and talk to
people."

One thing that helped us establish a state of mutual ease
was Dick Neal's presence on the staff. Chosen for his ability,
not for his color, the way he handled himself was an asset.
He knew that many Indonesian students preferred to take
their training in Europe because they had been warned that
they would be given a bad time in the U.S. The less sophisticated thought black men were still slaves. When they saw him
with us, some of them actually asked if he was a slave, brought
along under duress. Open, relaxed, and honest, Neal told them
the truth. It was far from an ideal picture, but it was a lot
better than the one painted by anti-U.S. propagandists and
Neal believed that in time the race barriers in his country
would collapse. Meantime they could see that he lived with us
as one of us, professionally and socially.

It seems odd that in this particular place, where we were
received with so much enthusiasm, we played our one Unfriendly Game.

Perhaps it was because they had managed to stir up so little
feeling against us that the local Party Communists were determined to show us up. They had advance word of our non-
prowess in sports. We didn't mind that. What we did mind
is that they sent in a crack team with orders from Communist
Headquarters to shellac us at all costs. For once, we determined to win.

Kuharic and Neal took the day off. They delivered pep
talks to the team. No fumbles today, no casual happy play.
We were in this one for blood.

Bloody it was. The Communist team pulled every trick in
the book and the umpire was a Party man. Dick swears he

still bears the scars to this day. But we did win. Somehow our two embattled stars called on resources they hadn't known they could command. It was by a narrow margin—but it was victory. The Sumbawans were delighted, and Mala had yelled so much and so long he could scarcely speak.

The very last act we performed on Bima, Sumbawa, was one of emergency mercy. During the final few days, McCannel had set up an office outdoors in Raba, outside of Bima. His equipment included a kitchen table, a bench, and a flashlight. His patients were legion. Fifteen minutes before he was due to close up this village clinic, an American nurse working with him saw a small boy who sat so quietly to one side he had not been noticed. She asked an interpreter to question the child and discovered that every day for a week he had walked twenty kilometers to reach Raba hoping that someone would take care of him. He was nearly blind, barefoot and hungry.

McCannel found that the boy's eyelashes were growing inward. Rushing with him into Bima, he sent out a call for the island's Dr. Tan. It was just an hour before sailing time. The launch was bringing in the last patients and on shore the staff was winding up and packing.

Hastily nurses reassembled instruments and prepared a table in what looked like a summer camp kitchen. Tan stood by while McCannel operated. The boy lay stoically under local anesthetic showing no fear. When it was done, Tan took over and promised to follow all McCannel's instructions. McCannel was rushed by jeep to the launch.

Across the water an eight-piece high school band lustily rendered "The HOPE March" composed in our honor as a farewell serenade. Sousa's best could not have pleased us more.

Music was part of our memories of all the islands: groups singing to us; the delight we took in singing with them; Johana Vettoretti's valiant efforts to tune her western voice to local music. Music, said Dr. Hanan, pathologist from Phoenix, Arizona, sounds especially sweet and sharp in the Indonesian nights.

On a short field trip into the jungle beyond Bima, he had been invited with some others to the house of a Chinese villager for dinner. "Afterward our host sang 'Falling Leaves' and explained that it is a song written by an Existentialist philosopher in France. There was something infinitely touching about the sight of a Chinese standing in the jungle dusk singing in French and explaining the song in English and Indonesian." Then, afterward, the Americans and the Indonesians held hands in a circle and listened while he chanted, "The morning star is risen, the evening star is gone. . . . Let's go home, let's go home."

We were not going home yet, not until we had been as far as Vietnam where the Communists and the Free World clashed in a shooting war. But our leave-taking was more than ever a painful and family affair. We had left our adopted Indonesian youngster, our symbol of friendship and healing and mutual affection, behind on Sumbawa.

It had been a most moving good-by.

When Mala's father came aboard to get him, he was astounded and overcome with joy. Wiping away his tears he smiled and shook hands wtih everyone he met and then kissed them on both cheeks. "I didn't know my own son!" he kept exclaiming to the interpreter. "Tall and well. So straight! I can never thank the American people for this." To Dr. Spangler he asked the translator to explain that Mala wanted to go to America with us. "I hope and pray he wins a scholarship one day to your land."

Mr. Kuzuma brought gifts with him for Dr. Spangler and for nurse Gloria Aguilera, lengths of woven material embroidered in silver. His wife, Mala's mother, was pregnant, he said, and if the next child was a girl her name would be Gloria Aguilera Kuzuma.

When Mala left the *Hope* we saluted him with the ship's whistle, an honor reserved for departing doctors and the President of his Republic. As the two of them walked down the gangway, the older man called back to us the words he had learned in English so that he could speak in the name of them all.

Said Mala Kuzuma's father: "God bless America!"

Part II

Washington to Indonesia

Chapter VII

"Bill, I trust you know what you are letting yourself in for!" said Dr. Elmer Hess when I first proposed HOPE. Nevertheless, I'm with you all the way."

He was, too, until he died. I didn't, of course, have any notion what I was letting myself in for or I might have quailed and dropped my extravagant notion there and then.

In 1958 Hess and I had been asked to become co-chairmen of the Committee on Medicine and Health, part of President Eisenhower's People-to-People program. I had worked before with Elmer, a bull of a man, internationally famous as a urologist and past president of the American Medical Association. He was also well known for being unmanageable, independent, outspoken, and a great believer in God and democracy. The idea of using moth-balled hospital ships for carrying refugees had come up before, but always as a government venture. We talked for days about this new idea of mine for a floating medical center and how it could help train people in the developing nations. For many, the God-given right of freedom had come suddenly, at the end of long years under colonial direction. Now, despite their difficulties, the fact that they clung to freedom was a plea stronger than any cry for help. "So we know what we want to do," said Elmer, "but how are we going to do it?"

Many months later Scripps-Howard columnist Inez Robb posed me the question: "Doctor, how does one go about getting a hospital ship from the government?"

Without stopping to think, I answered, "Well, you just ask for it."

It was almost as simple as that. I did ask. If the request was fantastic, the answer was even more so. It was yes. Implementation of that "yes" was what took such doing. But first, the asking.

I began with Bob Gray, Secretary of the Cabinet at the White House. His first reaction was "Are you kidding?" His second was to make an appointment for me with Secretary of the Navy Gates.

That one small bit of encouragement stilled my early misgivings. All right, I knew I would have to sacrifice all my personal time, a lot of my family time, and a part of my practice of internal medicine. I would somehow have to get a staff, doctors, nurses, supplies, a crew to operate such a ship. Enthusiasm, a bit of Irish luck, a persistent guardian angel, and a lot of help were all I needed. And prayers and pennies from thousands of Americans who must rally to the cause, as they had rallied to other causes, including CARE, National Jewish Relief, National Catholic Welfare, National Foundation for Infantile Paralysis, the Council of Churches Refugee Committee, and countless other amazing generosities.

Mary Routh Buchanan had been assigned to the Medicine and Health Committee as a liaison with USIS under the People-to-People program. She was due to be transferred overseas, but before she left she did everything she could to aid me. Her first emphatic suggestion was that I find a name, significant and easily translatable into other languages.

Bless Mary! Joe Geuting, the first new member of our "organization," agreed. Joe is an old friend and patient, an experienced association executive and son-in-law of the late John J. Raskob. We often met to discuss social, political, and religious ideas, and he counted himself in on my new project at once. At dinner, with our wives and over brandy, we threshed out the name. I think Joe suggested Health Opportunity for People Everywhere to fit the letters H O P E. A bit awkward, I thought, but the word HOPE was perfect. "Hope is the bread of the poor," said Thales. We had a name.

The very next day Eugene Zuckert, former member of the Atomic Energy Commission and currently Secretary of the Air Force, turned up in my office with a bothersome upper respiratory infection. This "cold" turned out to be the most chronic and expensive illness of his life. I was so steamed

Followed by an orderly from an island hospital, Joanne Hefelfinger carries a baby to *Hope* launch

Our mascot, Mala, with a straight back and gleaming teeth, stands beside a seated Indonesian friend
(*Courtesy Mavis Pate*)

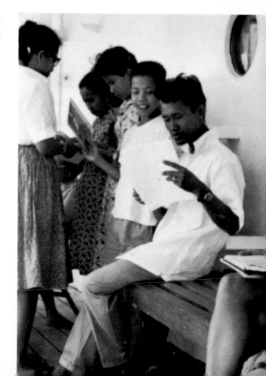

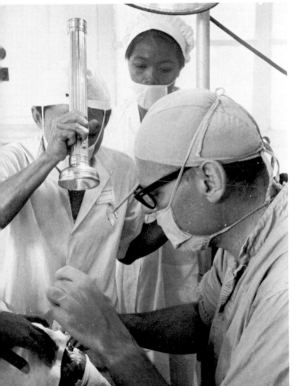

A team assembles for duty on shore. Conferring: Ann Roden, Dorothy Aeschliman, Dr. Marion Wier

Electricity was often inadequate in outer island hospitals. Intern holds flashlight for eye operation

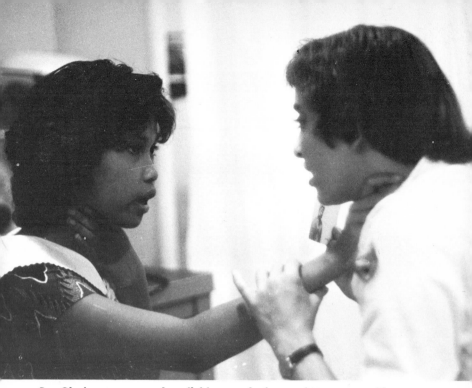

Sue Glocke coaxes sounds, syllables, words, from a thirteen-year-old,
unable to speak for years

When boatswain John O'Meara died we gathered on the fan deck
to consign his body to the Bandac Sea

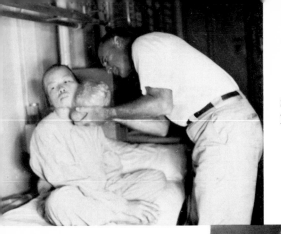

Sei came to us with a 6¼-pound parotid tumor . . .

. . . which Dr. Robert Pulliam excised . . .

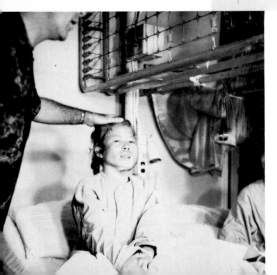

. . . making her the "Marilyn *Mun*-roe of Bima."
(*Courtesy Mavis Pate*)

up about HOPE that I forgot what the "Bald Eagle," as I called him affectionately, came for and so did he. "You didn't do a damn thing for that cold," he complained months later. "You just put me to work so hard I forgot it."

Work we did, that unlikely triumvirate, Joe, Gene, and I. Joe was 240 pounds of eloquence and idealism. Small of stature, Gene provided legal practicality and a cool, sharp mind. My finest contribution, I think, was a refusal ever to be wholly discouraged. Titular father of the plan, I was also father to three rambunctious boys, so until we had an office we met at the Zuckert or Geuting house.

First we needed "seed" money—enough to ask for more. On the night that Gene's wife Barby made the mistake of putting her head in to ask if we wanted a drink, we made her our volunteer secretary. Poor girl, her days of peace were over. She started sending our first "please" letters.

When I taxied to the Pentagon to ask the Secretary of the Navy himself for one of his 12,000-ton ships, I hoped the good weather was a good omen. As a former senior-grade lieutenant, I was well aware of my low rank, my temerity, and the jealousy with which the Navy guards her mighty possessions.

The Secretary, a tall man, dark and handsome and the very model of decision and efficiency, strode into his office a bit late.

"Good afternoon, Doctor," he said after I was ushered in. "I don't know what you want, but I hope it isn't much. I just had lunch with Admiral Rickover and I don't have anything left." He smiled.

"I don't know whether you will consider it much," I replied, having planned no strategy. "I want you to give me a ship you aren't using."

His expression did not change, but there was amusement on the face of his aide. I am certain at this point the younger man thought I had lost my mind.

"Go on," said Secretary Gates.

When my story was told, Gates turned to his aide. "Captain, I think the doctor's idea is a damned good one. Will you look into the law and see what we can do? I see no reason why we couldn't charter a vessel to these people—I hate to see them lying idle in Navy Yards. It would be out on loan, recoverable in an emergency." Then to me he said, "If this is possible, Dr. Walsh, we will give you every cooperation. Just remember, the Navy can offer you no personnel or funds. Our only possible contribution will be the vessel itself. Good luck to you."

Next I went to Dr. Snyder as the man we could reach closest to the President. He was a good friend of Elmer Hess's and one of the most striking men I have ever met. Straight as a ramrod at seventy-six, he held the toughest medical position in the world as Eisenhower's personal physician. Elmer had predisposed him to the idea, but he asked many a searching question before he agreed to present the suggestion to The Boss.

This was to be a project of the American people and we wanted to make sure no taint of partisan politics, so rampant in the capital, touched HOPE. Among us we tackled both sides of the aisle in Congress. Gene, a prominent Democrat, was especially helpful with Congressmen and Senators on that side. When we had real bipartisan moral support, we incorporated in the District of Columbia.

President Eisenhower and President Kennedy both believed that it is the obligation of individual American citizens to increase the nation's influence in other nations of the world. They did more than believe. They acted. As soon as he was fully informed what we were up to, we had a letter from the man who was then President of the United States.

THE WHITE HOUSE
Washington

February 11, 1959

Dear Dr. Walsh:

I have been impressed with the merit of the proposal developed by your Committee, which you have referred to as Project HOPE, and wish to commend you and the Committee for it and for the great effort both in time and money which your associates envisage devoting to this basically private project.

I have requested Secretary Dulles to provide for a central point in the Government to lend advice and assistance in the successful launching of the project and later in its orderly coordination with Governmental activities which are related to it. It would appear that a number of specific arrangements and understandings will be needed in order to insure that the project is successfully launched. When these are completed the Government is prepared to provide for the project a hospital ship in operating condition.

The State Department will inform you of the person who has been designated to work with you or with whomever you designate.

I wish again to commend you for the fine report and to wish the project the fullest measure of success.

Sincerely,
(signed)   Dwight D. Eisenhower

That day in February, 1959, we thought with this blessing from the White House our troubles were over. How very wrong we were.

Before we were done, we had direct or indirect relations with some twenty-six agencies or sub-agencies of the government, both Houses of Congress, and many members of the Executive Branch. This was all necessary to launch a project carried out on a People-to-People basis with no government participation. However, since we chartered a vessel owned by the government and attempted a brand-new type of technical assistance program, the government was very much involved. The great big stumbling block was No PRECEDENT.

I must say I think that to set a precedent in Washington is more difficult than to start a war. After all, we have been in wars before. I still wake up from nightmares with those words ringing in my tormented ears: No PRECEDENT.

Men like Christian Herter and Gates and Gray, Ambassador Jones, James Riddleberger, who was director of ICA, Secretary of State Dulles, had, of necessity, to pass on details to subordinates. Government is big and, for instance, the director of an agency which administers a $4-billion foreign aid program can scarcely know what goes on day to day in every department. Bureaucrats can be red-tape artists. When we urgently needed Riddleberger to cut the snarl of red tape a few of his men had managed to entangle us in, he was in the hospital.

When he was well again, he came to our aid, but meantime
we had nearly gone out of our minds with nit-picking, obstructionist, penny-wise delays, and if we had been dis-
courageable we would have given up.

One man, assigned to us as a liaison officer, all but accused
us of attempting to bribe him when one of our committee
members picked up his $1.75 lunch tab. I never did find out
what he suspected us of, but he conceived it his duty not
only to put roadblocks in our way, but to "protect" his
superiors from any information about those roadblocks.

When Indonesia was chosen as our first national port of
call, another obstructionist turned up in the guise of an
"expert." He had become one during a three-week motor
trip out of Djakarta. His conclusion was that we shouldn't go
there. Still another self-styled expert claimed that he was
important among the Indonesians, although none of them
has ever given me his name. He tried to stop us by stirring up
a controversy and then claiming that the controversy was so
serious the Indonesians ought not to let us come.

To relieve my soul of the venom that accumulated during
those next frustrating months, I have written this story in
full. It's an object lesson in what damage a few "willful men"
can do, especially armed with the magic weapon, "No
precedent," to prevent a good thing from happening. Still,
the HOPE is living proof that a willful group of men more than
equally determined that a good thing shall come to pass can
overcome such obstacles.

The public and indeed most civil servants want such good
things to happen. Once we were in the clear, the people
rallied to us. To get in the clear, so that we could present
a tangible, practical project to the public, we had to fight
for our lives. Well, we did, and I have expended my venom
on paper. Though some of that group still occasionally yap
at our heels, I shall file my documented anger in my desk and
go on to the happier task of recording how men responded
to our needs—big businessmen, government individuals, labor
leaders and laborers, blessed children who sold cookies and
lemonade to donate to our funds.

I asked for help as I had asked for the ship. I started

first by calling frantically busy executives, overcommitted to national and community work. "This is Dr. William Walsh in Washington. I would like to talk with you for a few minutes about something which is of interest, I believe, to you, and of even greater interest to your country." For some of the top men in the country, this was enough of an appeal.

Of those we wanted to be members of our board, only one refused. The very first man I saw, John T. Connor, president of Merck and Company, accepted at once and said, "I can't speak for the entire drug industry, but I assure you if this project gets in the water, the pharmaceutical industry will give you all the drugs you need."

General L. J. Sverdrup, president of an engineering company in St. Louis, was born in Norway and came to the U.S. as a boy. During the Second World War, he became General Douglas MacArthur's chief engineering officer. I was explaining what I wanted rather carefully, when he held up his hand. "You don't have to sell me, Doctor. I remember the people of those Pacific islands lining up by the hundreds asking 'needli, needli,' and sticking out their arms for precious injections. Our medical officers made more friends than anyone in the U.S. Army. Now, let's get to work."

We were very proud of our first board, which included George Meany, who appealed to all of organized labor to help us and arranged for me to talk before the 1959 AFL-CIO convention in San Francisco.

When the USS *Consolation* was actually chartered as ours, *The New York Times* ran a three-column story and picture on the front page. *Time* magazine followed with a story. The pieces of mail coming into our office jumped into the thousands. Volunteers turned up in droves. Our one secretary was swamped, but now she had help. From that day on, we were under a marvelous pressure from which we have yet to be relieved.

There were *still* roadblocks, put up by certain incomprehensible antagonists. The awarding of funds to the Navy for demoth-balling and rehabilitating the *Consolation* finally went through, but as consulting agency members they stuck their fingers into the matter of spending the funds. Take one incredible example. The Navy basic supply list included two dozen beer-can openers. Our nit-pickers demanded this item be struck from the list. The Navy assured them that "luxury" was not involved. Crews on any ship were permitted to buy beer on board when off duty. There have been honest errors of judgment involving millions made by bureaucrats in spite of the great care taken in foreign aid agencies. I wondered how they could spend time marking off an item of two dozen beer-can openers suggested by the Navy for the *Hope*.

Nevertheless the *Consolation* was readied. In due course she would depart from Seattle to San Francisco. There she would be officially and finally turned over to us. And the *Hope* would sail.

Meantime we stepped up our campaign to get what we needed. We propositioned doctors, and selected nurses from an astonishing landslide of volunteers. Twenty pharmaceutical companies gave immediate funds and pledged drugs. One manufacturer of cartons and packaging machinery presented us with 80,000 half-gallon milk cartons to set on the counters of stores all over the U.S. emblazoned with HOPE and a brief appeal for money. These began to fill with nickels, dimes, quarters, dollars. Thirty-seven companies teamed up to give us the machinery that would process sea water and, by the addition of solids and fats, transmute it into milk—our Iron Cow. We stumped the country. Foundations, corporations, fraternal organizations, churches, labor, management, and people responded.

A bunch of boys in a small California town formed the first HOPE group, and it's still going strong, though the founder has left to be a page in the Senate. The boys gave picnics, car washes, and basketball games. $400. Little girls baked cookies and sold them to neighbors. $6.87. Ten juniors in Illinois put on a musical show. One city staged a toy fair with the goal of $10,000 to put one staff doctor aboard the *Hope* for a year. There were golf tournaments, lunches, balls, fashion shows, bridge parties, moonlight cruises in the name of HOPE. Sixty firms donated supplies—not surplus, but what we ordered. Money rolled into the makeshift office where the beginnings of a professional staff began to help our volunteers. Committees were formed in dozens of cities. It was not and never would be "enough" but it was a great start.

The time came for me to make a preliminary survey of the country which had been selected first among those that asked us to come: Indonesia. In February, 1960, John Spreckelmyer, who was to be the *Hope's* hospital administrator until his health failed him, and I set off to see where our dream ship was actually going.

Chapter VIII

That trip confirmed everything I believed about HOPE. Even in a short time we could make a vital contribution in Indonesia and whatever we contributed would be well worth it. We would be helping a proud and intelligent people toward a better future. Indonesia could, I thought, become the salvation of the Orient if the Communists did not win their fight for its control. It is an undeveloped paradise. If its new freedom lasts and the nation grows strong and democratic, it is a potentially powerful ally strung out over an area of thousands of miles.

The Indonesian islands total over 3,600. There's no official figure because new ones constantly erupt from the sea. Each island seems greener and more fertile than the next. Drop any seed in this soil, they say, and it will grow.

At present, need is as great as potential. Twenty commercial aircraft service, or try to, 90 million people over that sprawling sea expanse. Fifteen hundred-odd physicians try to provide medical care. (Next time you call your family doctor and he doesn't get there for a few hours, think how it would be if you waited weeks, months, years.) Overcrowded cities burgeon in the midst of rich, uncleared jungle. Lushness of soil does not prevent a cripplingly deficient diet. This nation has tremendous problems, which it is facing with courage and optimism.

At one major conference, I saw their new democracy in action. The table was set up in a large U, with Minister of Health Satrio at the head of the table. People were seated pretty much according to protocol and seniority and the Minister simply started at one side and asked each one for his opinion. All of them protected their pride. They were anxious for the *Hope* to come, but no one wanted to admit how much she was needed. I was assured over and over that although their medical problems were vast, they were developing the trained men to cope with them. This exchange was welcome, but they felt much better when I assured them, in my turn, that we would learn from them as much as we taught.

There was internal disagreement as to how we should operate, as well as some all-out opposition to us. I stressed that we were a teaching and training mission and that we wanted only to help those who wanted to help themselves, not to show off our modern medicine and perform charitable miracles. We had many other invitations, from Korea, Formosa, Pakistan—and it was no reflection on the skill of their men that we had chosen Indonesia first.

In the end we worked out a partnership. HOPE would not bring "all chiefs and no Indians" as some of them feared. We would come as a training mission, but patients would be taken care of as part of the training. We would go as far into the outer islands as we could. SS *Hope* was ours, and we were invited to their country. They would pay the taxes, port charges, dock charges, internal transportation, and the salaries of local personnel. It was a true partnership.

As invited guests, not government employees, we could take full advantage of the respect and courtesy offered by the East to guests. A guest is sacred.

The eastern hospitality offered Spreck and me had been lavish. We were entertained by Indonesia's top men. But what remained with me most strongly were my personal impressions:

The wet, torpid heat peculiar to the tropics. The smell of

the islands, a dank pungent odor, compounded of jungle moisture, charcoal, kerosene, and of bodies sweating from too much hard work in such heat. The very water smells of it.

Driving through Djakarta, a typical teeming Oriental city, you find the main street bisected by a canal. People wash their clothes, their bodies and take care of their excretory functions in the same water. It is dirty, slow-moving water. The pollution begins in the streams that feed it, coming down from the high, clean mountains through village after village. Debris and garbage collect from every upstream settlement. When water reaches Djakarta, where children dive joyfully into it, it carries typhoid, dysentery, and every conceivable water-borne disease. In five years the present government hopes to decontaminate the canal and the streams, but in the meantime it is a pity the Indonesians are such clean people. If they do not have plenty of water that is pure, they will us any rather than none.

I remember the noise, a sort of muted shout that fills the air. Laughter and singing and endless talk and the horns of motor vehicles trying to clear their way through throngs of people and the traffic jams caused by *betjaks*. *Betjaks* are the Indonesian taxicabs, two-seated, hooded contraptions, each one pushed by a man on a bicycle. The Chinese control the syndicate and rent them to the drivers, who pedal them, live and sleep in them. A *betjak* pedaler is as indifferent to pressure as a New York taxi driver. The difference is that he does not shout back, but ignores you with the most polite and placid air in the world. "Blow and be damned, my dear sir."

One Saturday in Djakarta I was driving with Dorothy Allen, wife of the ICA Chief of Mission, when a whistle blew. Everything stopped. People climbed out of whatever they were riding in and soldiers appeared in the middle of the streets. "Heavenly Father," I thought, "we're caught in a revolution!"

Dorothy burst out laughing. "Oh, Lord, Bill, your face. Nothing's wrong. Every Saturday at twelve that whistle blows and everybody stops and cleans the streets. In half an hour, they'll blow the 'all clean.'"

That's one way to get your city tidied up and you can't say it isn't democratic in a way!

They don't practice democracy as we understand it—yet. When I talked to Foreign Minister Subandrio, we spoke of the need for mutual understanding. We should not be impatient with new nations. He felt that someday his country could develop our kind of government by the people, but that with a largely illiterate population, new to freedom, a certain amount of paternalistic guidance was very necessary. The danger of even the most benevolent paternalism is that it becomes entrenched. There is also danger of mob rule if there is no discipline and no tradition to control freedom.

I had a chance at that time to iron out certain misunderstandings on the part of the Americans who were official representatives of the U.S. in Indonesia and who were somewhat suspicious of us. At first Spreck and I had been treated by them rather as if we had a sort of noncontagious leprosy. We needed the cooperation and sympathy of American officials in Indonesia—and, for the most part, in the end, we got it.

Before I had to leave for the U.S. to prepare for *Hope*'s launching, we had done enough to make me confident of our reception in Indonesia. Committees had been organized in key cities, Indonesian and American officials won over, preparations well begun. Even so, I wished I were sextuplets. My full time was insufficient. HOPE needed a man lecturing constantly in the U.S., one who did nothing else but handle her affairs in Indonesia, one to go ahead to Vietnam, and one to stay in Washington. We hadn't the funds for such an executive staff. We, all of us, gave what we could and "made do." I made do with myself and as full a schedule as I could possibly manage.

Many generous people have credited me with selflessness and sacrifice since I have devoted myself to this work. It's not as unselfish as all that. I don't and never did think I was going to "save the world." I am blessed with a wonderful wife and three sons and a successful medical practice. I have also been through a war to protect my country so that I could have such a family and such a practice. Selfishly, I don't want my sons wallowing in mud, digging for their lives. I don't believe our Lord will permit a nuclear holocaust, but I do believe it is up to us who are free and blessed to help bring about a world in which there is no reason to have wars.

My country has a great heritage of revolutionary freedom. It has prospered in freedom. Christian precepts are part of all western civilization, whatever our personal religious beliefs: "Do unto others . . ." "Suffer little children . . ." But, I think, not since Pericles said it of the Athenians 400 years before the birth of Christ, has it been possible to say of another nation's citizens, "We are alone among mankind in doing men benefits, not out of self-interest, but in the fearless confidence of freedom."

That is why we did succeed in floating the *Hope*. That is why, in spite of all the hazards, we eventually reached Sumbawa, and began to get somewhere near our own ideal of such a ship.

Chapter IX

The *Hope* was our heroine and soon we were all to become her supporting players.

She was a splendid sight in the San Francisco harbor on September 12, 1960, the day before her christening. When my wife and I drove into the Navy Yard the *Hope* sat just aft of a new Navy cruiser fitted out with missile-firing weapons. The contrast between her majestic whiteness as a warrior of peace and the cruiser, a battle-gray deterrent to war, brought a lump to our throats. My wife's eyes were glowing and she pressed my hand.

Captain Jack Windas, loaned to us by the American President Lines, looked like a storybook Master. Somewhat over six feet, handsome and stern of countenance, he was hard at work plotting a course that would avoid monsoons and studying how to operate the ship with the greatest economy. He wanted to be sure and get full value for every Project HOPE Foundation dollar.

"I can't say she's as tight as I would like," he said to us thoughtfully, "but she's a seaworthy old girl."

Both Windas and I knew her history and I had met her before. Starting life as the *Maine Walrus,* she didn't carry that absurd name very long. The Navy took her over in May of 1945 as the USS *Consolation,* hospital ship, technically AH 15. By the time she reached Okinawa in October, she was streaked and stained all around her immense red crosses. I boarded her to get a required physical checkup.

"You been scared on that picket line out there?" asked the doctor.

"You bet your life," I replied grimly.

My health duly recorded as excellent, I went back to the picket line.

The *Consolation* (530 feet long, 71½ feet wide) in Honshu embarked a thousand poor devils who had sweated out four years of war behind Japanese barbed wire. They were Americans, British, Australians, and Dutch and they were not in good shape. After that she shuttled for the Fifth Fleet, rode out one typhoon and skirted another, until there wasn't much more to be done in the Pacific, and she was transferred to the Atlantic Ocean. For a while she trundled Navy families to Navy bases. After that she lay idle at Hampton Roads, Virginia, except for exercises in the Caribbean and the Arctic.

During the Korean War, she took part in the Inchon landings for the United Nations, the Wonsan and Hungnam operations, and in 1951 was docked in San Diego to have a helicopter deck added to her superstructure. Fifteen miles north of the 38th parallel, "Operation Helicopter" began. For the first time in history battle casualties were flown from the fighting front to a hospital ship in minutes, to save countless lives. She was on the job until after the truce and added up the tremendous score of nearly 19,000 patients.

When she sailed for San Francisco, in April, 1954, she was due for sea-pasturing, but war caught up with her again in August. On April 10 she was cleared for Vietnam, to

evacuate refugees from the North. When these people disembarked in South Vietnam, they could not have supposed
they would ever see the *Consolation* again. Once more in
Korea, she picked up a final complement of wounded, and
by the time she berthed at San Francisco in December, 1955,
she was battered and outdated. For nearly five years since
then, she had lain "out of commission" with her marine and
medical instruments imbedded in black grease.

The old girl had her medals: the Republic of Korea's
Presidential Unit Citation, the Vietnamese Ribbon of Friendship, the Navy's Occupation Medal (Asia clasp), and ten
engagement stars for service in the Korean War.

Now she looked fresh as a daisy, all painted up and ready
to go. "But," said Jack Windas, "what about those hospital
wards? We can't touch them, you know, except at a cost of
overtime, overtime, overtime. We can help some, but it's
primarily up to you. And I'm not sure about the inventory of
your medical supplies which are going into No. 1 and No. 2
holds. By the time we get into the area of operation, I'll have
the ship functioning and well. I've got a wonderful crew of
engineers. I'm responsible for the ship and over-all command,
but I'll try not to interfere in the hospital area."

Cups of coffee in the wardroom are S.O.P. When I was
medical officer on a destroyer, I got used to eighteen to
twenty cups daily. Now after ten minutes with Jack Windas,
fifteen years after, I found I had already down two cups
and was reaching for a third. Finishing that, I left him and
went to "inspect" the ship with Helen. I was happy. Windas
was the best captain any ship ever had, and I knew it.

Topside the noise was incessant. Winches turned and giant
nets swung up over the side. Heavy boots drummed on the
decks. Men shouted. Machinery growled, whined, and subsided, and the roar of San Francisco's traffic could be heard
as accompaniment. My wife and I scurried below.

Quarters were tolerable, though not lavish. Most cabins
were fours and each had a desk and at least two drawers
for belongings per inhabitant. No private bath existed except
for the Captain and the Medical Director, but we were sup-
plying bathrobes. Sixty-one human beings were going to

share these quarters for a year. Others would come and go.

The big classroom was inspiring. A hundred and fifty chairs, with side arms for note-taking, were ready for the Indonesians and Vietnamese who would come to learn and to watch the TV screens which hung behind the lecture dais. There was visual-aid apparatus for us. Classes in the strange languages we were going to encounter would give us at least please-and-thank-you familiarity. Air conditioning made the room cool and fluorescent lights bathed the air while rubber tile on the floor muffled our footsteps.

Steel bulkheads in the companionways had been painted a pleasant beige trimmed with dark green. Even in the tropics, they would look cool. Red lettering brought the future close—all the habitual directions were already stenciled in both English and Indonesian.

One wardroom was ninety feet long and thirty wide. It was "sexless" open to both all of the staff unless we had visitors and distinguished guests on board. Someone had hung American scenes on the walls, a purling brook, a mountain blanketed in snow, a western landscape. The nurses' wardroom was also pleasantly furnished. Rattan chairs had chintz-covered cushions and there were card tables and a player piano.

A dining room is only as fine as its food, ship or shore. We had reluctantly decided on a freighter menu, to keep the budget down, but as it turned out our Chief Steward, Mr. McGorian, assigned to us along with the crew by the American President Lines, was a culinary genius. At $1.87 a day, he fed us magnificently—and American food would become very important after we had dutifully eaten Indonesian TNT or such delicacies as barbecued dog.

In the hospital wards, Helen and I got a jolt. They were a mess. At least the matresses seemed first-rate, but the bunks, suspended on chains, were far lower than standard hospital beds. There was minimal room for chart racks, and equipment maintenance would have to operate in what I can only describe as a closet. But Leo Haney, who had resigned from the Navy to ship aboard the *Hope*, was also a genius, an all-American genius who could take anything whatever apart, mend it, and put it back together again.

Only a few of our people were yet aboard and the first one we ran in to was Marylouise Streicher. As chief nurse she was one corner of the *Hope's* administrative triangle. The other two were Hospital Director John Spreckelmyer and Medical Director Dr. Paul Spangler.

In any shore hospital it would have been a perfect team. Spreck is a solid, energetic, and frequently merry man who seems ageless, but he already looked gray with exhaustion from his unusual duities. After traveling with me, he had taken charge of the pharmaceuticals. Never have so many boxes arrived so fast from so many places, and never has an inventory been so impossible. Now this poor man was climbing in and out of holds and up and down six decks of steel ladders in a last-minute crisis.

Paul Spangler, a retired Navy captain, white-haired and bespectacled, was a charmer as well as an excellent surgeon. He fussed cheerfully about whether there would be three men assigned to him with sufficient talent to make up a barbershop quartet, but he also seemed confused and tired. I thought when he got out to sea his habit of command would take over.

Marylouise was fresh as the *Hope's* paint. She had done a perfectly marvelous job of selecting our nurses, twenty-two of them. As a personnel director, she could not have been beaten.

The trouble was that this trio would be called upon to meet situations demanding the most extraordinary physical stamina, as well as the ability to react with flexibility and speed to unprecedented problems and to remain in intimate communication with a large staff—something seldom if ever required under normal conditions. Age, ill health, and the inability to communicate fully when necessary affected the orderly working of this top trio. Lord knows, this is no condemnation! What they each contributed is beyond price. And when it was necessary to change the administration under emergency circumstances, it speaks for what they had already done and for the HOPE ideal itself that everything went smoothly.

As for Marylouise, her choice of nurses was the finest con-

tribution she could ever have made. She corresponded, inter-
viewed, and winnowed the applicants. You would really
have thought that the nursing profession was being offered a
"free vacation." Instead they were invited to spend a year in
a trying climate under difficult conditions, assigned to cabins
with strangers, drawn by alphabetical lot, at half salary. Most
of them thought they would not be paid at all.

The questionnaires went out months before the ship was
demoth-balled. Besides checking on qualifications, there were
leads designed to reveal temperaments and attitudes. Marylouise also looked for talents to be enjoyed communally—
singing, dancing, bridge, painting, sports, playing musical
instruments. The ship was bound for a world of dusky skins.
Prejudice must not be part of any girl's baggage. She selected
those she would interview and then had to ask her selections
to wait. "Stand by."

They stood. One young woman who was transferred from
the Middle West to California was so superstitious about not
pressing her luck that she vowed not to nag for news for
six months. When she finally checked in, Mrs. Streicher had
fiinshed interviewing on the West Coast. The candidate flew
at her own expense to Chicago, and got in five minutes ahead
of the deadline.

To those she finally chose, Marylouise tried to give an exact
picture of the trials and tribulations, but she herself didn't
know the half of it. She didn't warn them they would be doing
labor customarily left to hired huskies, scrubbing and scraping. When she told them to bring "about three times" what
they would need for a single summer, she hadn't counted
on personal laundry arrangements limited to that washer
and dryer through the ladies' W.C., and the rusty water. One
nurse said that when she finally arrived home and her mother
saw her lingerie, she was so scandalized she threw it away.
And nobody brought enough shoes. Tropical mud was murder
on shoes.

In deference to the ship's generators and to eliminate fire
hazards, curling as well as pressing irons were taboo. Marylouise honestly thought there would be a beauty parlor aboard,
but there wasn't. Sometimes the girls felt as if they had really

joined the Merchant Marine, as technically they were required to do.

Each nurse who was accepted had to have able-bodied seaman's papers, a "merchant mariner's document," cleared at a Coast Guard station.

One of them, Nancy Campion, went through this in New York. At Bowling Green she proudly handed over her credentials saying, "I'm from Project HOPE."

"What's that?" asked the officer. Then he sent her across an alley to Trinity Place where seamen check in. She was the only girl there and was quite conscious that the men were thinking, "Oh, no. It can't have come to this." After denying that she had ever been arrested for Treason, Sedition, Espionage or Sabotage, and answering another pound of paper questions, she was fingerprinted and her identification photograph was rejected. "Real pretty, but it won't do." The seamen's official photographer made her look like a candidate for the nearest brig.

Her brothers, who had been in the Navy, applauded her acceptance. "Know what you're entitled to now? The privilege of scrubbing decks."

That turned out to be more accurate than Nancy thought when she laughed at the sally.

A week before the *Hope* sailed, at the time of her dedication in San Francisco, these twenty-two chosen from among 2,000 applicants, began to arrive—from Wisconsin, Arizona, Maryland, California, New York—tall and short, fair and dark.

What a group of able-bodied seamen they turned out to be. I suppose it is always true that men achieve their ideals when they do because of women. It was because of her women that the *Hope* pulled through from San Francisco to Sumbawa. Women, I humbly salute you.

Chapter X

Somehow even our flags were ready on the day of dedication.
We had thought the American President Line would fly its
emblem, but at the last moment they told us we could have
our own Foundation flag. Artist friends designed it overnight
and friends who could sew ran up the first three, by hand.

President Eisenhower had asked Vice-President Nixon to
represent him, which Nixon was happy to do though he was
in the midst of his presidential campaign. He had been in
the part of the world to which we were going. For the rest,
Mayor Christopher of San Francisco, Joe Geuting, Ernest
Breech, president of the Ford Motor Company and a member
of our board, Len McCollum, chairman of HOPE's board,
and I would speak before the Vice-President did. Three
minutes, we agreed, and over.

Outside the St. Francis Hotel, several of us waited for
the Mayor, with whom we were to ride in the cavalcade.
His Honor went by a different route, and we barely made
it, commandeering an official car and policemen to get us
through the streets, sirens screaming. At the shipyard, I
joined Admiral Russel waiting for Nixon. When his car arrived, the Mayor rode in the back seat with both Nixons.
There was no room for Russel or me. The Admiral was not
disturbed by plans gone awry. He had another car ready and
we proceeded to the reviewing stand in that. Mayor Christopher forgot that he was supposed to go ahead to the stand
and welcome our distinguished guests. He stuck to the Vice-
President. I had been told to stand by the Nixons for the
official photographs—there were hundreds of photographers—
and I firmly did so. We looked pretty funny, the Mayor and
I, jockeying politely for position.

Nixon reviewed the Honor Guard and then we took our
places on the stand, more or less in order. The other speakers
kept to the timetable, having labored to confine themselves

to three minutes which is much harder than thirty. I'm afraid I didn't. I got carried away by the urgency of my feelings when I began to talk about the need I had seen. As I sat down, I mumbled an embarrassed word of apology to Pat Nixon, who was on my right, but she absolved me with the tears she wiped from her eyes.

The Vice-President began to talk about the needs of new nations and of what HOPE could mean. He had feared we would never get the ship out, in spite of the support we had. It would have taken the U.S. government, he said facetiously, at least five years to mount such a program. Facetious or not, I knew he was more than half serious. He was wholly serious when he spoke of the world's children and the world's needs. Then he read a letter from President Eisenhower, a generous and emphatic statement in support of HOPE, and at last gave the order for Captain Windas to raise the colors. The American flag rose on the stern and the HOPE flag, a moment later, fluttered up the mast over the bridge. At that instant, the sun blazed through from the clouds and the *Oklahoma* roared out a ten-gun salute over the "ruffles and flourishes" of a Marine Corps band.

Nixon's aides teetered nervously and tried to get him away, but Nixon talked about the ship for another quarter of an hour as he shook hands with everybody. An hour late, he drove off to campaign in Portland, Oregon.

In the week that followed, between dedication and sailing, we had last-minute problems. We would have preferred to schedule our departure a month later but our contract with the government had required us to take possession at once and to delay now would cost us a minimum of $1,000 a day. There were still details to settle with the American President Line. They would make no profit, but they had an obligation to their stockholders to insure them that they would not operate us at a loss. That meant giving the Line more money than we could spare, and leaving ourselves short. How much dared we gamble?

Essentials continued to arrive in such quantities that all hope of packing systematically was abandoned. We did not want to be caught in the Far East with our supplies down.

Foreigners do not expect Americans ever to be short of anything. A host nation may take a certain glee in being asked to
remedy American deficiencies and, on the one hand, it's wise
to admit we are not perfect. On the other, at least a degree
of perfection is a very good thing.

The last loads went in No. 1 hold helter-skelter and on
top was dumped a year's supply of rice in sacks too heavy
for human beings to dislodge. In one ward overflow dunnage
was stacked to the ceiling. All this caused trouble later, but
in this hectic time order was sacrificed to haste and the need
to get it all aboard: the fresh vegetables donated by the
Pacific growers, the canned food donated by the canning industry, as well as the endless medical supplies.

One crisis hit us the day we opened the ship to importunate
visitors. Spreckelmyer told me no alcohol had been delivered,
for medical purposes or for drinking. Our benefactor, Hiram
Walker, had sent the promised load to San Francisco but the
tax officials would not let us have it. We had no license to
"export liquor."

You can't run a hospital without medical alcohol. That was
more important than the fact that our staff members were
entitled to have drinks at the ship's bar and that we would have
to do a certain amount of official entertaining overseas. We
had not spent a nickel of our funds for any of it—it was a
gift—but we needed the gift. The tax officials would not
budge an inch.

Go to the top in a crisis! We got hold of the liaison man
between HOPE and the President of the United States and
asked for a special ruling. Bob Merriam whistled and said,
"I'll get it."

The warehouse was thirty miles from the dock. Tax officials
refused even to let us move the cases as far as the dock
until they had that ruling.

Sailing day came. Cranes worked on steadily. Visitors poured
aboard. Staff members tried to find their way to their cabins
through the crowd. I was down in the boiler room, the only
place free of intrusion, with Joe Geuting and the officials of
the American President Line. They had estimated on running
the ship at cost, but there was still the question of a guarantee

against losses. We had to give them half a million dollars before the *Hope* cleared port. It meant going for broke—and counting on raising more in time. There was no choice. We settled on their terms. Then I headed for deck as Jack Windas ordered all vistors ashore.

For his "medical crew," as he called us, and their families, Windas held a last ceremony. I took the microphone and spoke to them, my voice hoarse with emotion. Speaking from my heart of sacrifice and medicine and mission, I raised my eyes—to see a cargo net high in the air bulging with wooden cases clearly labeled "Hiram Walker." My hands tightened on the microphone. I was the only one facing in that direction. Completing a true statement that we were facing hardships and trials in the name of an ideal, I saw the net disappear below decks.

At twelve minutes past four on September 22 the SS *Hope* pulled away from Pier 50A, her flags fluttering. We flew the stars and stripes and our own handmade banners with their hands-across-the-sea device.

Captain Windas noted that the temperature of both air and water was 62 degrees, the sky clear. Between fountaining fire-boats and beneath a flight of Navy jets, we moved on past the battlements of Alcatraz and under the Golden Gate Bridge. Land faded into the mist and the *Hope* steamed steadily east.

Now we all began to meet each other. Like delegates at a convention, we wore name placards to introduce ourselves. Roommates sorted themselves out and inquired about each other. At the two dinner sittings, places were assigned and we met our dining salon neighbors. Groups formed in the lounge later and someone banged out tunes on the piano.

Besides the doctors and nurses, four medical secretaries, and the technicians, there was a camera crew of eight men to document the journey and two State Department guests who would, in the week between San Francisco and Hawaii, brief us on Indonesia. Francis Joseph Galbraith spoke the language and had served as political officer in the Embassy at Djakarta. Arthur Goodfriend was the author of *Rice Roots*, recommended reading. And there were two Indonesian girls,

selected by Minister Nugroho in Washington, who booked
passage with us in exchange for giving us lessons in their
language. Also, as an observer for the board chairman of the
People-to-People Foundation, there was Basil Littin.

We planned, of course, to be in full operation as a hospital
by the time we reached Djakarta. On this first cheerful night
nobody knew how far from that we were. At drydock in
Puget Sound, the vessel had been put in "operating condition"
as specified by President Eisenhower and the Navy. But
operating for what? We were well afloat, but the hospital area
had scarcely been touched.

I had foreseen that the work would be strenuous and the
adjustments difficult. Borrowing an idea from the Navy, I
insisted that when the sun was well over the yardarm, at
four o'clock, the bar be opened and we have what the Navy
calls Happy Hour. Our eleventh-hour alcohol was served on
the honor system, a chit for a self-poured drink. So far as I
know, no one ever abused the privilege or got too happy, but
they needed that hour very much indeed.

Every piece of old hospital equipment from the Navy was
in splendid working condition, unflecked by rust, but you
had to get at it. As protection, it had been packed in black
grease and the grease had solidified. In the hospital area,
walls wore an ancient patina of soot and the decks were
worse. Many new essentials for the hospital had been dumped
in No. 1 hold, and for a long time when anything was missing
we said it was "under the rice." Until the cranes began working for us in Djakarta harbor we couldn't find out for sure.

For the Catholics aboard there was daily seven o'clock
Mass served by Father Magner and for all of us seven-thirty
or eight o'clock breakfast at which we got the world's news.
Then "chiefs" and "Indians" alike climbed into fatigues and
began to chip at grease, mop floors, wash walls, and organize
supplies. The crew couldn't help us and if we didn't do it
ourselves no one would.

We had daily classes, but there wasn't time for more than
a bowing acquaintance with that musical language, to learn
words like trouble, *kesukaran,* pain, *sakit,* eyes, *mata,* head,
kepala, dizzy, *pusing,* sleep, *tidur,* and the one that became

most familiar—*obat*, medicine. Along with this practical vocabulary we mastered please and thank you and a code of manners different from ours.

When it was warm enough to sunbathe, we had a sunbreak and our two Indonesian girl teachers dashed around with us in shorts and bathing suits, looking very much like the Americans except that they were smaller boned and more delicate.

Then long before we were remotely ready for one, we had our first patient. Ann Roden, a tall, slender young nurse from South Bend, Indiana, was too sick to raise her head. One thing we had was doctors and they diagnosed her trouble as an abdominal cyst, which should come out as soon as possible.

Nurse Mavis Pate drafted two assistants and they scrubbed and sterilized every inch and corner of the smallest operating room in three hours. The machines were not ready for general anesthesia and Ann was conscious when she was wheeled in. Captain Windas stuck his head through the double swinging doors and asked whether the motion of the ship would complicate things. He had slowed down already. Ann smiled at him lovingly for his thoughtfulness and Dr. Spangler said there was not enough swell to unsteady his hand.

Ann lay under a lamp the size of a searchlight, looking up at a tangle of overhead pipes stenciled cabalistically OBVD DISCH and DISC VENTS, accompanied by arrows. The walls needed paint. Hands which were making ready in the emergency were more skilled with scalpels than brushes.

By Ann's side Mavis Pate's wide, strong face was framed in an antiseptic cap; Ann found her Texas drawl comforting in the strange atmosphere. Dr. Spangler started to work and tension mounted. Halfway through, Mavis heard a plop and saw that a pipe above the light was leaking. She grabbed a towel and held it so that water would not drip on Ann. The last few minutes of the operation were a race between surgery and the broken plumbing.

Our people were all tops in the most modern hospitals in the world. They found themselves in an outdated mess. "Play it by ear" became the *Hope*'s byword as everybody pitched in.

I mean everybody. The cameramen volunteered in hours off from their own work. "I'll be free for two hours this afternoon. Where do you want me?" One cameraman turned to the nearest nurse when he was on all fours scrubbing the X-ray room and said, "Don't you dare tell my wife!"

Three days after first patient Ann was rolled through the cream-colored corridors back to her own bed, the seas were logged as heavy and the drainage system collapsed entirely. The toilets flushed endlessly and spewed on the floor; the showers dwindled to a trickle.

Bud Littin heard a rumpus below and shouted down to know what was going on. Frank Galbraith yelled up to him that there was water in an operating room three inches deep and horrors in the water. Bud descended and was handed a mop. Could the HOPE Board Representative do less than the State Department which was up to its ankles in gook?

Eighty-five mattresses were later lugged upon deck, cut loose from protective covers, aired, turned, and beaten. Top berths, which we could not use, were lashed permanently to walls except in the Intensive Care Unit which required ideal conditions. Here the upper bunks were removed, bolt by bolt. Then the cameramen lugged away the heavy metal frames.

Nobody gave up in the face of missing supplies or lack of familiar equipment. No stands to hold intravenous bottles? The uprights where the berths had come out were the right height. Wire coat hangers were twisted and hung onto them. Not enough bottles? Everyone ate peanut butter for days to get the jars which were the right size. No operating room drapes to cover patients during surgical procedures? Two industrial sewing machines were found in the crew's tailor shop and nurses turned seamstress.

The secretaries sewed, too. Johana Vettoretti, chief secretary, realized the day before sailing that no uniforms for the four of them had arrived. Spreck thought Marylouise Streicher had ordered them and she thought Spreck had. Johana offered to rush to Sears and get some, but couldn't get an order to do so. What did arrive at the last minute was an odd lot of blue and white seersucker dresses, a gift from WACs at Treasure Island. They had survived World War II, were long, dreary, and badly worn. At sailing time, the girls were reduced to wearing them. Now they refitted and shortened them for use in Indonesia.

That was strictly spare time. The secretaries were on call day and night. All the stores had to be checked, recorded, and categorized, even though what was "under the rice" would change these records.

Everything was done running up and down stairs. The elevator only worked if you were where it happened to be. You couldn't summon it by ringing. Nor was the public-address system very much use. Its only speaker was on the bridge, technically off-limits to the staff. If you wanted somebody, even in an emergency, you went and found him.

When I say "we," you understand, I could not be with the *Hope* as much as I wanted to be. I was, as I should have been, wherever I could be most useful to the Project, the Project which now belonged to us all. Sometimes I fought continuing Washington battles, sometimes I stumped the country for funds, sometimes I was on the ship and sometimes ahead of it.

This first voyage I had been in Washington and then flown ahead to Hawaii. When I heard the full story of that first week, I wondered why our women simply did not get off in Honolulu. Preparing for the doctors who would fly in and out, rotating as a working staff, they had slaved at filthy, back-breaking jobs. Now, after having seen them at work for many months, I know they would never have quit.

When they landed in Hawaii I realized they were a tired bunch, but I thought that was all. No one made me aware that a crisis was developing. Perhaps no one thought it was. Certainly, although they looked weary, they also seemed radiant when they walked down the gangplank onto Aloha pier at half-past eight in the morning of September 29. This was already their HOPE, their ship, their project. I never saw such a bunch of winners. They shone. They really did.

Chapter XI

At least they had a glorious breather and a swim at Waikiki.
The stop in Honolulu was scheduled only for refueling, but
Dr. John Holmes, head of the enthusiastic Hawaiian Hope
committee, protested that the Governor himself had dedicated
September 28 and 29 to Hope and that we couldn't duck
away.

A standby skeleton staff took turns showing hordes of
visitors through the ship while the other staffers took to the
colorful shore. Tours were arranged for them and there was
time to raid the shops, to try the surfboards, to necklace
themselves in flowers, the beautiful Hawaiian leis. Nurse
Nancy Campion, a lovely brown-haired girl, bought a native
muu-muu for Ann because Ann's bandages were too bulky for
a dress, and the camera crew hired an enormous limousine
("soft as a bed") to take Ann around, but after an hour
she had to wobble back to her berth. I think it was that day
she started the afghan we all remember with such affection.
For ten months it was always in her hands when she was
off duty, bright contrasting colors as vivid as Hawaii's.

The photograph albums started there, too, the ones I'm sure
every single member of the *Hope*'s staff carried home. I don't
remember seeing anybody without a camera wherever we
landed. We are a nation of shutterbugs.

In Hawaii we lost Galbraith and Goodfriend, who had to
fly back to Washington. Good-byes were warm. They were
among the comers and goers who kept shifting the pattern
of personalities. Over seventy-five rotators were with Hope
first to last, and perhaps without such shifts cliques and en-
mities might have grown up. Miraculously they did not and
the system of rotation kept us supplied with protean talent.

Three new faces came aboard in Honolulu: Dr. Mary
Glover, X-ray technician Renée Beauregard, and physiothera-
pist Sue Glocke. When the *Hope* sailed a day, seven hours,

and twenty-one minutes after she landed, they, as did everyone, tossed flower leis into the sea honoring the superstition that this guaranteed them a return to Hawaii. I waved from the dock along with hundreds of well-wishers. My job was to return to Washington and then fly out to Djakarta for our medical debut.

Three hours later a seaman who had been discharged in port was discovered still aboard. Lurking behind the back of a sofa in the women's lounge—or in a lifeboat, according to another report—he was found in an excessively euphoric state. Captain Windas had the pilot describe a long, slow turn back into the lei-littered waters of Hawaii and the large, burly, and far-from-agreeable seaman was decanted into a ship's net and lowered over the side onto a tug. Unfortunately a photograph of him descending like limp cargo made the front pages in America and we lost temporary prestige as well as hours of time.

Sue Glocke's mother had died only a few weeks before, but she had decided to leave Beekman-Downtown Hospital where she was working in New York and go through with her HOPE commitment. A small, dark girl with warm eyes and a quick smile, she was pleased with her department. The equipment was excellent and only needed demoth-balling. It took her half a day to scrub down the walls with disinfectant, a job she would scarcely have found necessary in Mayo's, Warm Springs, or Beekman, her previous hospitals, but that seemed unimportant. Her roommate, medical technician Florence Mudge, was helping to haul fifty-pound watertight cases out of holds. At night she and Sue fell wearily into tiny berths.

After going to church one morning, Sue found a Mass card lying on her bed. A special service would be offered for her mother. At this memorial service, Johana sang the Bach-Gounod "Ave Maria." "We are really one large family on the ship," Sue wrote home. "A comfort . . ."

Religion was an integral part of the ship's life. The corridor on which Bill Anna, our Protestant chaplain, and John Magner, our Catholic chaplain, lived was affectionately christened "holy alley." Here these two Ministers of God offered private spiritual guidance to anyone who came to them and kept posted the score of their year-long bridge game which filled the intervals when they weren't occupied.

Even with the pressures which were stepped up in the knowledge that we were soon to open as a hospital, the entire ship's complement attended daily services. Johana was the star of the choir, though she had forgotten to bring her music along. Accompanists who could play by ear were not lacking, and she sang Gregorian chants from her prayer book as well as adding to the entertainment at evening gatherings.

All small breaks were welcome from the hard labor that became routine. Sue Glocke regularly visited Mr. Dow, chief operator in the radio shack, a grandfatherly man who drew cartoons in his spare time and, busman-on-a-holiday, amused himself as a ham radio enthusiast. Dave Palmer, his assistant, shared Sue's interest in anthropology and was working toward his M.A. When later an ambitious scheme hooked the *Hope* with the continental U.S. by radio-telephone, with ham operator William Green in California to make patch connections, the first person who talked to her family was Sue. It helped stave off bouts of homesickness.

On October 6, the international date line crossing gained for all of them two extra blessed hours of sleep. As if to make up for that luxury, Sue volunteered to check off the crew who were due for immunization shots, and the next day, when a leak in a sewage line delayed her own work, helped in the operating rooms, unpacking, sorting, and washing clamps and suture scissors.

The *Hope* had reached the part of the world where there were no twilights. The sun dropped "like thunder" leaving an afterglow of brilliant color. Added to the tight schedule was one appointment on deck: 5:45, watch sunset.

Twice a week there were old movies and on Saturday evening, October 15, there was the usual foolery initiating neophytes who had never before crossed the equator. Engineer Strohacker was Neptune and Dr. James Yates was Mrs. Neptune. The Reverend William Anna played Royal Baby and film-crew member Harvey Genkins was Davy Jones. Costumes were impromptu for the ceremonies which turned pollywogs into shellbacks and shellbacks into royalty.

The name Balikpapan, when it was announced, produced a dash for maps. The *Hope* would refuel there in North Borneo and her medical crew rejoiced that the stop was scheduled for Sunday, a day when duties were kept light.

They saw lush green hillsides dipping down to a town and smelled the pungent aroma of land in blossom. It was their first eastern port. Disappointment was bitter when the Captain reluctantly informed everybody that officials would permit no one to leave the ship. Apparently the Borneans on shore protested, for very shortly afterward the ruling was rescinded.

Shell Oil, while their fuel went into our tanks, kindly supplied buses and townspeople turned up with cars to take our people through the city. As soon as any visitor set foot on a street, he was swamped by children, grinning, friendly, curious. They swarmed like locusts, lining up in patched clothes to have their pictures taken and indicating, dumb-show, that they longed to peer through the binoculars and field glasses many of our staffers carried with their cameras. As far objects showed near, they giggled with pleasure.

At first the town seemed a European version of any middle-sized city, with prosperous houses lining shady streets. But as you neared the marketplace, away from the homes belonging to men in government and oil, the odor of flowering trees was overpowered by that of dead fish, food past its prime, and rancid coconut oil. Across the way from open food stalls, a dentist squatted in the dust, his equipment a pair of pliers, a wrench, a drill, a hammer, and bottles of colored water. As a lure for customers he had set out two cups of teeth.

The native section was indescribably poor and fly-infested. Canals of stinking, stagnant water provided drainage, and, as in Djakarta, children used the water to play in.

They were, just the same, the merriest small fry imaginable. Tagging after us, they christened us, setting up a cricket chant that was to greet us in every eastern port: "Hopie! Hopie! Hopie!" Before we even set to work, we were named—the Hopies.

By nightfall the engines throbbed again. The *Hope* plowed on, sliding through black water past the mast and stack of a sunken ship, casualty of one of the revolutions which erupted there intermittently, and on toward Java. The crew had been working as long and hard as the medical staff to correct malfunctioning in their part of the ship. Repairs, which to our distress cost us $12,000, were done. They had to be. Captain Windas was as careful with our money, other people's money, as a man could be, but only half the plumbing had been in working order, only a quarter of the air-conditioning system. There was trouble with boilers and generators. This was now under control, but all was not well with the *Hope.* There were only three more days before Djakarta and she was not yet a hospital.

Worse than that, somehow, some way, communication between departments and between department heads and their staffs had broken down. Without calling a general meeting, the hospital administrator sent off a cable from Balikpapan to me in Djakarta: IMPOSSIBLE ACCEPT PATIENTS DJAKARTA.

Chapter XII

The blow could have been mortal. So much depended on that first impression. We were eagerly awaited, but there were many who longed to see us fail, who would take full advantage of failure. We would lose face irreparably in Indonesia if we failed in its capital.

Any neutralist area has a strong Communist element. In the outer islands, Mao Tse-tung was a hero. In Djakarta, Sukarno was popular but many of his loyal followers were mystics and fatalists. They wanted us to succeed, but if we did not, it was the will of Allah.

As advance man for the *Hope,* I had wound my way through snarls of red tape, helped by an indefatigable HOPE committee. Though I am not very diplomatic by nature, I had succeeded, I thought, in controlling my temper and my impatience. Dancing a diplomatic minuet in a slightly elephantine fashion, I had refrained from stepping on toes to the right or the left. We had our chance in Indonesia, a great one—but not if we took no patients in Djakarta.

By God's grace I had foreseen that the staff would be too worn out to open the wards, laboratories, operating rooms, and services the very day the *Hope* landed. The Minister of Health, furiously impatient, agreed with reluctance to forty-eight hours' delay during which visitors would tour the ship. Five thousand guest passes were issued to assuage general disappointment.

That gave me two days. I didn't know what I was facing, but the one word I refused to tolerate in connection with the *Hope* was "impossible."

At four-thirty in the morning on October 16, a month to the day after the *Hope*'s dedication, Guy Kirkendall, acting director of HOPE in the East, and I went to meet her. From the deck of the pilot boat, with light just streaking the sky, we saw the proud, yare lines of our ship outside the breakwater. Pennants stirred in the dawn breeze and the letters of her name stood out against her white flanks. Ship or sepulcher of hope?

The rail was lined with faces. Within a couple of hours, the ship would be brought in touch with the shore and we would belong to the country we were visiting. No time for amenities. We must act.

The rundown I was given disclosed a state of near-paralysis. Efforts to get ready for our opening had been Herculean, but no one person had taken hold to integrate these efforts. I had failed to spell out authority and responsibility as I should have. Each department separately had been reduced to despair.

In Djakarta I had promised that we would treat, demonstrate, and teach. Thirty Indonesian nurses were coming aboard for training. Why should they come with us if we were not what we claimed to be? There might be no teaching mission.

The jungle telegraph would carry news of any failure to the outlying islands, where Communists would make the most of

it. Would patients there come to us at all? There might be
no healing mission.

Within twenty-four hours the first group of rotating doctors
would arrive from the U.S. to take their turn with us. If they
saw us inactive, would they go right home again?

HOPE had been floated on contributions and needed more
at once. If we seemed fraudulent, why should the public give
us more money to carry on?

My chief nurse hammered away at me. Persist in opening,
she said, and half the staff will resign. Did I know what they
had been through? They were exhausted. Things were simply
not ready. There was rice in the hold.

I called the nurses together in the big classroom. Without
shame, I threw myself and the project on their mercy. Could
they, would they, work around the clock and *somehow* make
ready to take patients in time to meet the commitment I had
made in their names?

There was a second of dead silence. My heart dropped to
my boots. Then those women stood up and cheered. A girl
spoke to her neighbor in ringing tones. "Well, thank good-
ness! This is what we came for."

One thing I had learned to my utter dismay was that nursing job assignments were in a muddle. No one had been
notified exactly what she would do, although everyone had
been asked to submit "programs." I turned to Mrs. Streicher's
senior assistant.

Claire O'Neil is a strongly built young woman with a wide,
ingenuous face and an Irish grin. She was trained for command, had served with the Navy Nurses Corps, and had set
up a new hospital in her own home town of Concord, New
Hampshire.

"Can you take it from here?" I asked.

"Certainly, Doctor," said Claire.

"Thirty Indonesian nurses are due on board tomorrow," I
reminded her, "and with them thirty-five helpers and orderlies
to do the heavy work in the wards."

Claire's face cleared as if she had seen a vision of heaven.
"I was fretting myself sick over how we could manage without any help!"

The *Hope* is dedicated to her mission of teaching and healing . . .

. . . and sails to the Orient from San Francisco

A litter patient hoisted to the *Hope's* deck by special lift steadied by solicitous hands

After dizzy trip, litters are lined up for assignment to wards. Nancy Campion talks to patient

Hope's launches transported personnel, patients, visitors, across the tropical seas

Chief nurse Claire O'Neil gives
last-minute instructions to Indonesian chief nurse Gan en route
to clinic

Everyone knew who was boss in
the operating rooms—chief surgical nurse, Mavis Pate

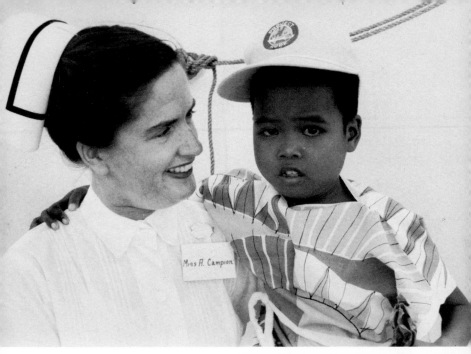

By the time Sana left *Hope* in Nancy Campion's arms he had won the hearts of Captain, crew, and staff

Watching operation beamed to classroom over closed-circuit TV: Drs. Ratcliffe and Walsh, President Sukarno of Indonesia

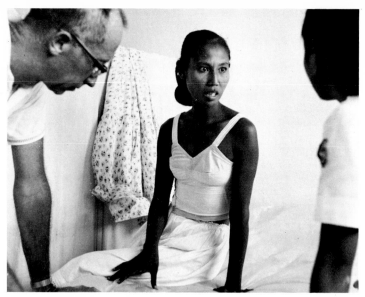

(*Above*) We had to refuse the incurables. A woman on Timor hears verdict of Dr. Benner from a nurse-interpreter. (*Below*) Dr. Youker and Technician Phillips instruct future radiologists in the use of X ray for diagnosis

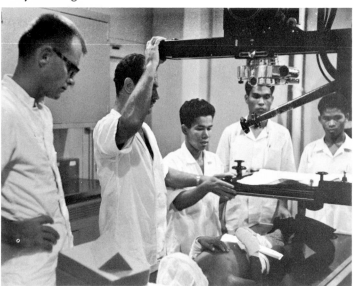

HOPE's gift of milk clutched by a hungry child is symbol of American concern for undernourished everywhere

Below the Plimsoll mark Al Adams supervised the machine which produced milk from sea water. We called it The Iron Cow

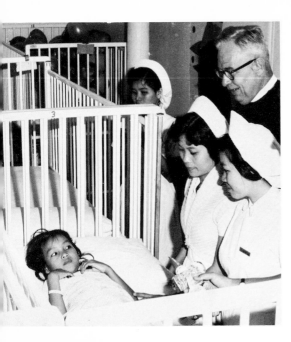

Fathers Magner and Anna
offered all who came to
them spiritual comfort and
guidance

I groaned. It seemed impossible that my deputies had not told these girls that they would have plenty of assistants, to clean wards and help with the grueling routine of sick care.

"Wow," exclaimed Claire happily. "I'd better get going."

Fran Harris had not known that she was in charge of nurse education. When I told her, she said she was afraid she couldn't do it. The projected curriculum, she had been told, was aimed only at the highest university standards. I assured her that this was wholly impractical. First we had to find out what caliber nurses we were training. Close-tolerance specifications would come, if at all, very much later. "Well, Doctuh," she said in her contagious Texas twang, "then, that's just fine. Don' you worry, now. We'll do all right."

Mavis Pate came next. There was no hint of panic in this calm, unassuming girl, strikingly professional even among her peers. "I didn't know I was to be chief surgical nurse," she said quietly. "I'll need three nurses assigned to me for the operating room and central supplies."

"Will an Indonesian do for one?" I asked.

"Certainly, Doctor, in time," said Mavis realistically, "but not right at first. We'll have to move too fast."

"Just let me know how many cases you can take on board the day we start," I said, relief washing over me as burdens fell one by one into these capable hands. "I'll have each rotating surgical specialist talk to you first and check his own instruments to give you a hand. Then can you make up a week's schedule?"

"Of course. But I must bring up one problem, Doctor. We have no draw sheets for the operating room." You can no more operate without the big sheets that fit over patients, with openings to isolate the operating field, than you can operate without scalpels. I was about to groan again, but Mavis was making a report, not throwing in the sponge. "We've located bolts of muslin and huck toweling. We have two sewing machines. If you approve, the girls will work all night and sew extensions on the small slit sheets we do have. We can rip up pillow cases to make instrument stand covers, if you don't mind, and I think double bed sheets will work as table drapes. Okay, Doctor?"

"Okay!"

Mavis smiled her slow, friendly smile and used the same words Claire had. "Don't you worry, Doctor, we'll do all right."

I was not to worry while they contended with the emergency. Though she herself had understandably collapsed under it, I blessed Marylouise again for her choice of nurses.

Touring the wards, I found the pediatric department closest to ready. Marion Wier and Dick Elliott, downright, sturdy New Englanders, had taken over that area and the library. Some other sections, in spite of dogged work, were in a state of appalling disorganization.

Again, in radiology, I found Tim Lally all set to go, but Dr. Dennis, in pathology, lacked essential chemicals and vital parts of his colorimeter. His reports of both omissions had not reached me in Washington, though I got a request for more phonograph records. My face was black as thunder, but he, too, said, "Don't worry, Doctor. They may turn up on board."

"If they don't," I promised, "we'll borrow here and order replacements from Singapore."

Captain Windas, in this crisis, volunteered manpower to lend a hand for the next two days. The cameramen performed fresh prodigies of day labor. Leo Haney seemed to have six capable hands instead of only two and sped from corridor to corridor responding to cries for his mending genius. Al Adams, herdmaster of the Cow, had his machine all set to produce prodigal quantities of milk. Spreckelmyer rushed all over the ship, working until I was afraid he would collapse, which he nearly did. Afterward he gave some first-rate lectures and then we had to lose him or risk permanent damage to his health. Marylouise Streicher, worn out and overwhelmed, left us, but everyone else stayed.

"What made you stick it?" I asked Claire much later.

"Just when I was about at the end of my tether," she said, "one of those blessed cameramen backed me into a corner and told me that what we did in the next few days would decide whether we would be infamous or famous. And then you came along and put it up to us just the way you did."

Today the nurses of the *Hope* are famous.

Meantime we had to get through Djakarta.

At least we presented a smiling and united front to several hundred Indonesians lined up along a shed to greet us as Captain Windas maneuvered the ship to the dock. Tall, white-headed Dr. Soekarjio, Dean of the University of Indonesia Medical School, delivered the opening address. His native shyness seemed to affect the microphone which conked out completely. When Colonel Dr. Sjarif Thajeb took over, rendering the speech into English, the microphone came on full blast. The crowd applauded both versions with equal enthusiasm. I spoke, warning our friends that we brought no miracles with us (refraining from the comment that it would be a three-star miracle if we accomplished anything in their city).

On board, that morning, our guests were so charmed with the Iron Cow and its miracle of rich, tasty milk from sea water that they overlooked the fact that the rest of the setup was still pretty sketchy. President Sukarno had particularly asked for milk, and the Minister of Health, General Satrio, was benevolently cherubic when he inspected the Cow that afternoon. The cartons carried a double billing: the milk was from the American people and the Ministry of Health of Indonesia. Satrio, throughout, was our very firm and able friend.

HOPE would be in Djakarta just two weeks. I had to explain to the city's physicians that we could not, under any circumstances, live up to their ideas for putting 500 patients aboard us. They accepted the necessary strictures reluctantly—and so did the doctor-rotators from America when they arrived next day. One group of four had rendezvoused in Honolulu, to be intensively briefed there by another "expert." This Cassandra once visited Indonesia. He claimed the natives were much too fiercely superstitious to let us touch them. No doctor wanted to come so far, disrupt his practice, receive no stipend, and find nothing in the way of medical experience waiting for him. They hadn't come to see Djakarta, her red-tiled Dutch roofs blazing in the sun, or for a tropical vacation. When I

told them we weren't preparing for a big case load on the
ship, they thought the Cassandra was right.

Though they were long-faced and weary, I decided to take
them straight from our headquarters to the RSUP, Rumah
Sakit Umum Pasat, or General Hospital, in town, where they
could select the patients they would indeed take care of from
the numbers referred to us.

As soon as Jack Tetirick, surgeon from Columbus, Ohio,
and the other three rotators saw the cases lined up, fatigue
and foreboding left them. It was a veritable museum of
pathology. Among those they chose were a four-and-a-half-
year-old girl with a spleen that stretched from nipple to pelvis
and a small boy with a huge localized Hodgkin's disease of
the neck. Tetirick asked an Indonesian doctor how they could
ever let a spleen get to this fantastic size. He answered, with a
slow smile, that they had been waiting for the *Hope.* This
was intended partly to remind us that we were already six
months late in coming.

I told Jack and all the others that now that we *were* here,
the watchword was "flexibility."

The first plan was to have each operation performed by an
American doctor followed by the same operation performed
by an Indonesian under his guidance. That might be possible
often, but hard-and-fast procedure just wouldn't do. We would
"play it by ear." In time each man worked out his own way
of teaching. This might have been wildly disorderly, but it
wasn't.

At 1:00 P.M., October 21, a line of olive-drab ambulances
arrived on the quay with the patients whose plastic wrist-
bands identified them as selected for treatment. And, by God,
we were ready for them.

Cranes had at last lifted out the rice and much that was
missing came to light. When a dock worker fell from a sling
unloading a neighboring freighter, he was carried aboard and
Dr. Spangler was able to take care of him. The thirty Indonesian nurses were installed among us, ready to go to work.
They couldn't do much yet except add to the crush, but they
proved quick, anxious to learn, and as charming as a cageful
of birds. Visitors flowed up the gangplank until Dr. Alex-

ander Sahagian-Edwards said, "Enthusiasm and curiosity may be what sinks us after all. It's like a Marx Brothers comedy to run, broken-field, from ward to ward."

That was the day we discovered how addicted Indonesians are to running water. In a country where streams run dry and then overflow in torrential rains, they bathe passionately when they can. We had our second group of patients washed on shore and dressed in HOPE pajamas before they were put in the ambulances. Later we found out that the first set had been just as carefully bathed, but no one had mentioned it.

By nightfall, on the 21st, thirty-seven patients, among them the boy Sana, with Hodgkin's, and Yuyu, the girl-child with the spleen, had been extracted from the showers, fed, and put to bed. Claire thought one very old man was having a dizzy spell when he started swaying his head uncertainly over the side of his berth and flew to catch him. He was trying to make his obeisance to Mecca. She borrowed a little compass brought aboard by another patient so he could be sure which way was East. Next day we installed one in every ward.

On the 22nd, Jack removed the massive spleen without knowing that Yuyu's parents were watching over our closed-circuit TV. When the operation was completed, nearly five hours later, they were so deeply moved because we had saved the child's life that they offered to present her to the *Hope*.

Another observer on that first day when we actually started to work was the President of Indonesia, Dr. Achmed Sukarno.

Dr. Sukarno and all Indonesians have reason for their pride in their children. When we got to know them as patients, we knew that anything we had been through, anything we did, was worthwhile. They make you proud of the human race and humbly aware of its potential.

One very small one cried on the table as he was about to be given anesthesia. As he wept, he repeated one liquid phrase over and over. Our surgeon asked the Indonesian doctor standing by what the child was saying, thinking it must be "go away" or "let me alone" or "don't, Doctor, don't." What the little boy said, over and over, was an apology for his tears. "Forgive me. Forgive me. Please forgive me."

Another seven-year-old needed an intravenous pyelogram, a kidney X ray requiring the painful injection of dye into the veins. There was difficulty in inserting the needle into the antecubital vein of his small arm and the puncture was repeated several times without success. This child also began to cry and the distressed radiologist suggested canceling the procedure for the day. When the youngster realized this, he sat up on the X-ray table, wiped his face, and pointed to a vein that stood out on the back of his hand which had not yet been noticed. The procedure was completed.

Sana was a sad-faced fellow. Like Mala he had been too crippled to find any joy in life. The tumor on the side of his neck was the size of a football and he did not remember a time when he could turn his head to the right. Children in the ward brought him toys and the camera crew put on a puppet show for him, but he did not even try to smile or speak.

Diagnosed from a biopsy section, the lesion proved quite possibly amenable to surgery and follow-up radiation therapy. California's Jack Ratcliffe, experienced in radical neck surgery, knew that Sana had become our earliest personal symbol of hope. We all wanted to see him happy instead of sitting in stoic distress, his eyes filling and spilling over, clutching a stuffed rabbit, the only toy he would accept.

When Sana was brought in, the lecture room on the other side of the bulkhead was filled to capacity with Indonesian students and physicians. All of us who could spare the time, staff, crew, and cameramen, stood in back. You could see the boy wipe his eyes, but he made no sound or gesture of protest. You could hear a pin drop.

For six and a half hours Ratcliffe worked in a temperature well over 90 degrees. A nurse mopped perspiration from his forehead with a cloth dipped in a bucket of ice. Dick Thompson, giving the anesthetic, damned the fact that he did not have the proper-sized endo-tracheal tube. Sana needed blood during the surgery and it dripped slowly. The tumor was larger than it appeared and tension grew unbearably. When, finally, Jack closed the skin, he and his Indonesian assistant smiled a little behind their soaked masks, but the outcome was still uncertain.

For twelve hours American and Indonesian nurses watched over him every minute. Sana waked in the morning. He reached for the side of his neck and a new expression came over his face. Speaking in Sudanese, he asked where the lump had gone.

We found out, now that he was no longer speechless, that Sana was not stupid, but very bright. The HOPE cameramen made a wonderful documentary film showing how one child had changed from hopeless to happy. Every time he turned his head to the right his eyes lit up. By the time he left us he had acquired and wore constantly a flowered Hawaiian shirt and a baseball cap bearing the Project HOPE insignia. At a special ceremony, Captain Windas spoke of Sana as a mascot and symbol. Then he presented him with the stuffed rabbit he loved. We all applauded Sana and he joined us, clapping back and laughing with delight.

Chapter XIII

If the annals of medicine weren't full of these individual stories of life-giving, most doctors would be unable to go on. We all tell them like rosaries and pray for more. Here or anywhere, it's the same with healing, especially of children. We cherished our successes in Djakarta where the dark side of our mission was darker than we dared think about much.

The medical fraternity wanted a floating Mayo Clinic. They sent us an undue proportion of wholly incurables from their museum of pathology to see what we could do. We had to refuse impossible challenges. Our limitations were definite. One Indonesian will never forgive us because we didn't bring angiocardiography equipment, which is highly specialized and requires a tremendous amount of X-ray film for each patient. In that intense constant heat, film is difficult to store even when there is enough on hand. It was against our whole concept to provide services which they could never duplicate, and I thought it particularly unwise to bring such equipment to a place where mass X ray was sorely needed. But that man had promised his patients we would have it and his status suffered.

Some shortages were mistakes. I have a fetish against bigness and hadn't wanted too large a permanent staff, but the logistics of rotating and of ordering what was needed were complicated by communication. I was not prepared for ten-day delays before a cable reached Washington from Djakarta and vice versa. Sometimes both supplies and people got lost. The Indonesian attitude was that everything would "turn up in time." Usually everything did, but often the worse for wear and long overdue.

Somehow we kept to the stiff schedule we set for ourselves, even on the morning when a fire hose broke and the nurses arrived to find the three operating rooms and the utility room under water. Everybody turned to again and we were ready to operate at 8:00 A.M. instead of 7:30.

We mounted four conferences daily on the ship and additional ones in the evenings ashore. Average attendance was over 200 and discussion was spirited. Many of our men formed close personal friendships with their Indonesian counterparts and the exchange of information grew intimate.

Indonesian surgeons are exceedingly deft, have a tender touch, and learn rapidly. Men with limited training in surgery were able to handle complicated procedures after taking part in only three or four demonstrations. Dr. Bergman, for instance, our urologist, taught his new friend, Dr. Oetama, techniques the latter had only read about. Now Oetama is an expert and teaches these techniques at the University of Indonesia. Ten per cent of the general surgery needed in Djakarta is genitourinary, principally because of the high incidence of kidney and bladder stones. With Dr. Bergman's stimulation, a program of research into the causes has begun.

As for us, we found opportunities we might have spent six

months in the U.S. just to locate. Our gynecologist, Dr. Myers, operated on more cases of choriocarcinoma than were diagnosed in the whole U.S. during the full calendar year of 1959.

Every day HOPE personnel made ward rounds at the RSUP. They returned full of admiration for physicians coping with so much on so little. Two nurse anesthetists had been badgering me for days about one piece of equipment. One evening Peggy Donahue came to see me again and confessed shamefacedly, "We really don't need it. I'm embarrassed because Priscilla and I carried on so. After seeing what these people use for anesthesia, I think we can do a bang-up job with what we have."

Leo Haney donated a day at the RSUP and when they found out he could repair anything in the world, they brought him just about that. Sitting cross-legged on the floor beside his toolbox, he fixed a Heidbrink anesthesia machine and, for good measure, installed a new fluothane vaporizer of which we had two, and a new gauge and regulator. The hospital for months had been reduced to using only ether. Now they could choose among ether, fluothane, or nitrous oxide. Cast-cutters, an autotechnicon, whatever needed fixing, he fixed, fetching extra parts from the ship when we could spare them and making parts himself out of whatever was handy when we couldn't.

It wasn't a one-way affair. They gave us what we needed when they could spare it, and even when they couldn't.

A wheeled stretcher which carried patients to and from the operating rooms had deflated tires and, of all foolish things to turn up missing among so many thousands of items, we couldn't find a pump anywhere. Or buy one in Djakarta. At once an Indonesian physician invited Tim Lally to dinner. Beside Tim's plate that night was a bicycle pump with a card in large, childish handwriting, "For the SS *Hope*." The doctor's seven-year-old son had sacrificed his all-but-irreplaceable pump to our needs.

Sometimes it was barter. From the local Catholic hospital, nurse-nuns came in a billowing group to admire our clinical laboratory. Sister Maria, looking wistfully at a pile of pipettes, remarked, "We could do seriologies if we only had some."

The HOPE pathologist said, "We're just as bad off. We can't for the life of us find any Kahn antigen and we can't do seri-ologies either." Next day the Sisters wangled fresh passes and came back again. While her companions formed a shield to prevent anyone seeing in through the open door, Sister Maria reached into the voluminous folds of her habit and brought out a bottle of precious antigen. Our pathologist, with a quick glance at the door, took the bottle and put a dozen pipettes in Sister Maria's hand. They disappeared in-stantly within the same folds. Everybody was happy.

In spite of an aura of disillusionment, the Indonesians really did their best to make our visit work out well. Heaven knows we were lavishly and warmly entertained—more often and more lavishly than we wished, given the amount of work we managed to do. The press, on the whole, was very kind, too, and appreciative. In an article headlined "Errand of Mercy," the Indonesian *Times* editorialized that HOPE was a mani-festation of concern by the citizens of the U.S.—for those less fortunate than themselves. "It will be a long time before this act of American generosity is forgotten. Welcome to Indonesia, then, teach us and guide us so that we may transmit to our people the forensic skills you have so carefully garnered. The East forgets many things but never, never loses its reverence for a teacher."

One thing we taught them inadvertently was that we, too, lost patients. We thought it was a lesson that would cause them to lose all faith in us.

From the beginning we had worried over what would hap-pen if an Indonesian died on our hands. That wasn't the reason, of course, why we refused incurables, but it was a nervous point. With hostility lurking so near to the friendship we were shown, a death might have profound effects. The Communists were already trying to stigmatize us as an Im-perialist hospital performing obscene experiments on helpless Indonesians.

One twenty-six-year-old woman with a very severe internal malignancy got through the checkup. Of course we never refused the possible, and we had managed to save—or at least to prolong the lives—of four similar cases.

Hers was an exceedingly rare type of carcinoma and surgery was fraught with danger because of bleeding in the
vicinity. We ran almost immediately into the dreaded complications of intractable hemorrhage and irreversible shock.

From noon until six in the evening, the American staff and
the Indonesians worked to stem the bleeding. Fourteen pints
of blood were transfused into her veins, and she was returned
to the operating room for a second time in a desperate effort
to save her. At six the Indonesian doctors left the ship, but
the Americans worked on with the American and Indonesian
nurses for another three hours. Then she died.

The nurses drifted silently away. Everyone was dispirited
and we were frightened that this one death would undo all
the efforts of two weeks.

In the morning, the harbor was like glass under a fresh,
bright sky. On the lovely shore, were we damned for what
must happen under the best of doctors?

Father Magner leaned on the rail, wondering and waiting.
The chief Indonesian nurse joined him. "Father, I can't stop
thinking about that poor woman dying. I'll never get over it.
None of us will. All of your people working like that for
hours and hours just to try and save the life of *one* patient!"

Her attitude reflected, fortunately, the general attitude that
spread through Djakarta. It wasn't the death they took note
of, but the valiant effort to prevent it.

Chapter XIV

We weighed anchor after "13 days, 05 hours, 06 minutes in
port," on November 2, 1960. It was a thankful moment. Nothing really untoward had happened. We had survived and had
a day and a half at sea before we landed in Surabaja.

A goodly crowd were at the dock to see us off. They were
friendly and full of warm wishes. Some of them came to say

good-by to our Indonesian trainees, who proudly wore Hope patches on their shoulders. These included the first-year class of the Bandung Nurses Training School.

The American nurses had been quite upset when the Indonesian girls were quartered separately. One of their ideals was to cross cultures and they wanted everyone to understand that we felt no color barriers. Crossing cultures isn't all that easy, and the Hopies discovered that the Indonesians had been alarmed at the notion of sharing their privacy with total strangers. They wanted time to get used to us.

Food turned out to be a bigger problem than language. English is the second tongue in Indonesia and even the least fluent among our Djakarta student nurses understood a fair amount. Hopies had shyly mastered key words in Bahasa Indonesian, a limited esperanto designed to unite all dialects and create a truly national language. But only a few Americans liked Indonesian food and the Indonesians, for the most part, only "ate American" to please us. They asked for a separate galley and dining room. By the time we left Djakarta the arrangements were both friendly and satisfactory.

Surabaja, 400 miles east of Djakarta, is come on suddenly from the sea. The harbor entrance shelters behind an island, Madura, and only after the *Hope* was near her mooring—next to a Russian ship with the hammer and sickle on her mast— did we see the sprawling town, like a series of villages grown together without plan or haste. The pace was leisurely there, and jasmine and bougainvillaea sweetened and brightened the air.

The people were pretty and friendly, but neither the local government nor the medical fraternity welcomed us. We desperately missed the presence of a man like Dr. Sukario in Djakarta, a senior medical figure who had made it his business to attend every class and conference. We missed the direct blessing of President Sukarno and Minister of Health Satrio. Surabaja's Mayor was a member of the Communist Party (the PKI). In Djakarta, the Russian Ambassador had inspected us thoroughly and doubtless he would have been happy to report deficiencies back to the Kremlin, but officially he said to me that this was a fine type of field in which our countries should compete. The PKI in Surabaja wanted no democratic competition.

The medical fraternity in Surabaja did not want competition either. Although they were quite aware that the Communist scare stories were nonsense, they had misgivings of their own. Their 1,400-bed main hospital is a good one and they are proud of a potentially impressive research center. They had no wish to be patronized, or to get themselves in wrong with the local Communist Party people.

Our reception was hasty and one of our Indonesian nurses advised us to leave East Java at once and go on to Bali.

The staff refused to yield without a real struggle. They heard that the University in Surabaja was celebrating the centennial of its medical school. Thirty-five of them—doctors, ship's officers, and nurses—went ashore uninvited and invaded the ceremonies. All dressed up, they filled an entire row and sat courteously listening to speeches in Indonesian for over two hours. The attitude of the Indonesian physicians abruptly shifted. After the meeting, our people were asked to the medical school fair. With their hosts and the young people, they played games at the bazaar, bought dishes and trays at the booths, mingled with the crowd.

From that time on, things changed. That simple gesture made all the difference. Dr. Anwar, the Health Officer, could carry out his plans to make us useful. Communist threats grew inaudible. A new group of Surabajan nurses joined us for training, most of them male, since orthodox Moslems may not be cared for by females.

At the first-rate local hospital, we were in for a surprise. We had expected mainly tropical diseases, malaria, parasitic infestations, leprosy, and the like, about which we could learn from them. These were present, but far more prevalent were the so-called diseases of civilization—peptic ulcers, hypertension, latent schizophrenia, heart trouble. It was hard to tell exactly why. Partly, I suppose, it was because the Dutch when they were ejected in 1949 left no one ready to carry on. The Surabajans had to take over ill prepared. There was also the ancient domination of the Malay female, still part of the culture in a city this size and more so in the hinterlands.

Boys suckle, or pull on dried tits for comfort, until they are close to puberty and marry almost as soon as they reach maturity. Above all, I think, however, these nervous disorders were induced by political tensions.

We had learned a good deal in Djakarta. In our rounds of Surabaja's city hospitals we daily selected all of our own patients. This prevented "prestige" cases from getting undue attention and opened the *Hope* to poor and rich alike. Visiting hours on board were restricted to two days a week, except for the parents of small patients. Our nurses stopped trying to live up to impossible American standards based on an economy of plenty.

"Know what I'm going to do?" Priscilla Strong asked. "I'm going to show the nurses on shore how to replace a soiled bottom sheet with the top one. Patients here are in clover if they even *get* two. My hospital at home would fire me, but not if they knew what's possible in Indonesia." At the same time Claire O'Neil was brooding over the possibility of covering the bare mattresses in a lesser local hospital with clean palm leaves.

At the University Hospital and Children's Research Center, Sue Glocke was impressed with schooling, play, and group exercises and she discovered a whirlpool bath for spastic cases. It wasn't used because no one knew how to use it though they wouldn't admit it. She invited the directors aboard to see how ours worked. Afterward they activated their own.

Hopies began to do a lot of mingling well below the official-entertainment level. They shopped in enclosed markets, finding their way without guards, and using their freshly acquired Indonesian vocabulary. Dorothy Aeschliman, Claire's second-in-command, had lived in China until she was fourteen years old. Chinese began coming back to her as she heard it spoken in this part of the world. She gabbled her way all over town and, against all caution, ate food cooked in the street over charcoal-filled barrels. "It's *very* hot," she insisted, "and can't be bad for you." Dottie, slim as a boy and with a perky quickness that contrasted with the deliberation of the Orientals, was one of the first of us to get truly close to them. She loved the East and wanted to live there again.

No one else was quite that sure of what they were saying and doing. Occasionally confusion led to strange places, as on the day when two of our girls wandered inadvertently into the Jungle, or red-light district. Gales of laughter warned them that something was wrong, and they retreated to more respectable neighborhoods.

I don't think we left an unmixed impression in East Java, but we managed against odds to leave a generally favorable one. Memories and mementos of our visit would serve the U.S. cause.

HOPE staffers had been active as far as Malang and Kediri as well as in Surabaja. Our last gifts were an electrocardiograph machine to the medical school; the first iron lung for their Health Service; a thousand medical books and periodicals. A large quantity of drugs and vaccines would be used for the follow-up treatment of 800 patients whom we had seen. Laboratory and dental equipment went to the University.

We had our last evening in the big-town civilization of Java before we left. The University provided entertainment for us by way of farewell. It was a kind of Godfrey talent show, with two crooners, a *wayang*—a puppet show depicting the struggles between good and evil—and an all-girl electrical band whose repertoire included "Sincerely." The girl performers wore skirts and blouses, the boys Brando-tight pants and suède jackets. They would have liked to demonstrate for us just how American they had become, but rock and roll was forbidden by law.

From this time on, for a while, we would be in places much farther removed from anything we knew. We were headed for the lands of leprosy and *dukuns*. The outer islands had few doctors and few schools.

Our first outer island was nearby Bali and we could not help thinking of it in romantic terms. Bali—the very name conjured up romance.

Part III

Bali to Djakarta

Chapter XV

Bali was Paradise Lost to us who were medically trained.

The island is marvelously beautiful and its people gentle and exquisite. They dance and sing and smile—happy people with timeless lives. Their years have 210 days and no one day is considered anyone's birthday. Every day is everyone's birthday. It is an island of temples. Religion is not for seven days—every day belongs to the gods. The Bali Hindu worships as he breathes his moist, flower-scented air. Bananas are there for the picking and rice grows richly in half-drowned bright green paddies, each presided over by a shrine. Western clothes mingle with native costumes, but almost no one wears shoes. Walking lightly on bare brown feet, the men are extraordinarily graceful, the women straight and sweet-moving as they carry their bundles on top of their luxuriant hair. Even the cows seem part antelope. They gather their feet under them and sail over ditches and fences.

It is a tourist paradise. Denpasar, the capital, has first-class hotels and perfect beaches. The people dance and sing for tourists without self-consciousness and everybody smiles. Foreigners are not threatened by disease on Bali—it is rarely of the kind you pick up if you are well fed and healthy. And the gentle Balinese do not inflict their sorrows on visitors. They are calm and complaisant in the face of illness and death.

Illness is so much part of their lives that the primary problem of the Health Department is to win them to take the simplest precautions, use the simplest preventions. There is a variety of foods but they do not vary their diet. It is easier to munch bananas and fix the abundant rice three times a day. Even if they are hungry, no one will touch the offerings of food for the spirits, piled fresh on palm leaves in front of every dwelling and each tiered temple. The languor with which they stroll so gracefully barefoot is partly due to rampant hookworm which attacks through the soles of the feet. Idyllic laziness comes partly from microorganisms which they have no stamina to resist and from infections that leave them debilitated.

What has been has been, what will be will be. Records are not kept and if you ask a patient how long he has had an abdominal swelling, he says agreeably, "Two days. Or maybe two months. Or maybe years. *You* decide, Doctor."

Cremation is part of their religion and that should be sanitary enough, but bodies are often kept for months in a small shelter in the courtyard while a priest decides when the time is propitious for burning and the family saves money to pay him. Someone constantly attends the body and sometimes the dead are washed on the swimming beaches.

Those antelope cows which look as if they could try for the moon give no milk and too little beef. There is no milk on Bali except that which is given by mothers who are often anemic.

The few doctors work so hard and well they put us to shame, but they have more than shortages of equipment and too many patients to deal with. The Balinese will not give blood or permit the transplanting of one part of the body to another. It is against their religious custom and they are peculiarly resistant to outside influences. While we were there we were anxious to offer our blood, but were told it would be no use. We could have drained every vein on board without setting an example they would follow. Families refused to give blood to save their own children.

The *Hope* lay in a cove edged with sand, soft and glittering. Palms ringed the cove and in the near distance hills rose in shadings of bright green to umber. Behind them towered the dangerous and beautiful cone of the holy mountain, Agung. Across water so clear you could see thirty feet into its depths, dozens of outrigger canoes rode out to greet us. Lithe brown men offered us coconuts and ripe bananas in all colors, red to green, and lengths of fabric and woven

baskets to buy for rupiahs or to barter for old pants, cigarettes, anything. Two men from the *Hope* slipped down among
them, speaking a sort of Choctaw-pig-Latin-Bahasa, trying to
pretend they were native traders. The Balinese loved the joke
and gave their sign of satisfaction—thumbs pointing skyward.

To cross the narrow reef, we used our World War II LCI.
The landing craft made a slow turn to the long pier jutting
from the beach. Grinning, sleek-skinned children spilled across
the sand to wave and chatter in Bahasa and Balinese mixed
with textbook English or disported themselves like otters in
the surf. Two blue buses, with the insignia of the Health
Department, waited to take us to Denpasar.

Intrepid and fatalistic Balinese drivers made the sixty
kilometers in an hour and a half. Bouncing and frightened,
HOPE doctors, nurses, secretaries, and technicians supplied a
Barnum and Bailey parade for the amusement of children
swarming from thatched huts under coconut palms. Small villages surrounded with cactus-topped mud walls turned out en
masse to cheer and women with burdens on long poles or on
their heads and a schoolgirl with a bottle of ink perched on
her hair swung their bodies toward us and waved, smiling.
Our first impression was of paradise.

Dr. A. A. M. Djelantik, health officer for the island and
one-man HOPE committee, met us at the General Hospital in
Bali's capital. Son of a prince and memorably handsome
member of a handsome race, he was a man with deep inner
serenity and profound concern for his people. In his opening
speech he pled for understanding and true cooperation and
then he made an explicit and honest statement of the island's
medical problems. They were terrifying. Malnutrition on Bali
was greater than anywhere else we went.

For a million people the government supplied ten general
practitioners, one surgeon, one oculist, one neurologist, and
three dentists. There were also two private doctors. Those
who worked for the government frequently supplemented tiny
incomes by seeing patients out of hours, and one of them, a
young man, averaged 200 a day. He was suffering from an
ulcer.

"Many wait for you with great expectations," said Dr.

Djelantik, "but be sure of one thing. Our patients don't expect doctors can do everything, but like patients the world over they expect that the doctor will be concerned about their complaints. Having heard about you, they will be eager to see you and I had in mind to make this opportunity as vast as possible by having you divided into teams and having these teams work with our doctors in our ill-equipped hospitals. I think that in this way the meaning of HOPE will be best served. Thank you very much."

A discussion of transportation followed, and we felt a note of constraint among the Balinese. We already knew the roads were bad and the number of vehicles limited.

"Look," said Jack Tetirick suddenly. "I'm perfectly happy with Indonesian food and I don't need air conditioning. I'll stay anywhere you put me on shore so that I can work better with you."

Every American there seconded him. The Balinese physicians exchanged glances and began to smile. Djelantik rose again and said, "Thank you, thank you very much. We were concerned that our food and accommodations would not seem adequate." Then, wreathed in smiles, he reached in his brief case for his alternate plans. Five mobile teams would operate from Denpasar, Singgaradja, sixty miles north on the opposite coast, and Padangbai, near the *Hope*. An emergency staff only would be left on board. For the greatest efficiency and use of our time, we would work directly with doctors in the hospitals, train nurses on the spot in the wards, and in the back country seek out *dukuns* and witch doctors. These native healers were, Djelantik assured us, often very capable obstetricians and skilled in bone setting. Furthermore they would welcome us (they did) and were anxious to improve their traditional ways.

Our people were grateful for time on shore to make friends, to do what these men had carefully planned in order to make the most of us. At Ramaj Umum Wangway, the main hospital, Dr. Noerah, resident physician, asked us forthrightly to begin by training two more hands to screen incoming patients at the clinic. His one good man couldn't handle it. To do so, we took over the endless lines of people and suffered the agonies of the arbitrary choices he encountered every day. If this one, then not that one. And however we hurried, so many were turned away.

"It's too awful," said Marion Wier, "to see a child with 105-degree fever taken home because the clinic closes while its mother waits for her turn. And when we reached one baby, we found it had been in convulsions for hours. We were too late."

To the other more "modern" hospital our first and perhaps most valuable gift was that of a fly swatter for the operating room. There were no screens and no traffic control. Surgeons changed their outer apparel, but observers and students watched close to them without even covering their heads. Nothing was sterilized except instruments, taken to a boiler in another building. Wounds which did not heal by secondary intention were considered complicated.

Our nurses set up the first post-operative Intensive Care unit in Central Hospital. "It was a terrible temptation to bring everything we needed from the ship," said Dorothy Aeschliman, "but we were dead set on leaving a system behind they would keep on using—we hoped. One thing we did leave was jars for dressing and salves. We sent word to *Hope* to please eat peanut butter everybody, three times a day and they did! The empties furnished the dressing cart."

Using pantomime worthy of Marcel Marceau, the girls bypassed the cumbersome process of translation, English into Bahasa, Bahasa into Balinese, and taught the Indonesians to take blood pressures, to turn patients to prevent post-operative pneumonia, to keep records, and to scrub however little water there was. Automatic recognition of the symptoms of shock and chill, color of skin, appearance of urine, state of fingernails, was drilled into the Balinese nurses. Some of them hadn't even known how to count pulses or read thermometers.

Reward came when Claire asked the Balinese if they would be able to keep our system going. Smiling broadly they replied, "Yes, indeed. We like it."

The hospital kitchen was an outdoor shack and dietician Hazel Wessel had to disperse thick coatings of flies before she could identify the food being cooked. According to Alex Sahagian-Edwards' wry description, our sanitation officer

Donald Snow "went screaming over the horizon, a broken man."

It was more than flies, lack of water, no refrigeration, and inadequate sterilization. "The state of their nutrition," reported Alex, "is unspeakable. They fall victim to any bacteria or organism. Malaria, leprosy, and parasites—and we were shocked by the rate of tetanus (lockjaw) which for most of us was a textbook disease. The first patient our pediatrician saw was an infant in a tetanic condition and one of the searing images of this trip is a roomful of mothers nursing rigid tetanic babies."

"I just wanted to cry," said Mavis Pate when she saw the wards full of people destroyed by yaws, leprosy, typhoid, babies gasping with pneumonia, their small bellies swollen from protein deficiencies, legs spidery from lack of vitamins, open sores on tender skins.

Hazel Wessel preached and argued with every parent she could reach to vary the children's diets. Soybeans grew on the island, but no one ate them. The children played catch with sea slugs and fish abounded in the ocean, but seafood was not popular. "What do you feed your children?" she asked over and over.

"Rice, *nona*."

"Please . . ." and Hazel would explain with flat Midwestern emphasis how important it was to give them other things. "What's that?" she asked one woman who refused her child a crusty-looking substance she herself was eating.

"Ground shrimp, *nona*."

"Give the baby some," Hazel begged. "It has protein. That's what he needs."

We unloaded 20,000 pounds of powder milk. We also donated quantities of a mixture which contained dried rice, soybeans, and other nutriments. It could be fried or mixed with water and baked. The Balinese promptly added peppers to give it flavor. Dr. Ratcliffe made the mistake of biting into one of the small green peppers they like eating. "The hottest thing outside Los Alamos," he commented. "I crashed in flames." Hotted up with these peppers, the Balinese pronounced the protein mixture, called "Meals for Millions," delicious.

The farther out from Denpasar we worked the worse it was. Water ran only two or three days a week through rusty pipes. Electricity was so feeble Ratcliffe operated on a rajah's hemorrhoids by flashlight. In one hospital, a single kerosene sterilizer came to a boil every two hours and only then could the instruments and the one needle and two syringes be sterilized. Oxygen was in such short supply that we had to participate in heartbreaking decisions: save one critical case today or hoard for three major operations tomorrow?

Dr. Ireton from Dayton complained about the shortage of supplies. "It was no fun," he commented, "to try and fix a fracture without any plaster." Nor was it any fun to amputate the rest of an arm and a leg from a patient attacked by a shark when there were no artificial limbs. Ireton's youngsters at home, when he wrote them, feared for the doctor's safety and were haunted by dreams of cannibals, leprosy, and sharks.

We nearly lost Marion Wier whose life is dedicated to keeping and making children well. In the hills she came on a religious observance performed before one of those exquisite temples. The kris ceremonial is a rite for boys between six and nine.

There were no western clothes worn by the large crowd surrounding the boys and exhorting them. Each boy held a kris, that evil-looking, sinuous dagger of the East with murderously sharp edges. Working up into a sort of catatonic frenzy, the boys writhed and stabbed at their bodies. As the frenzy approached a trance-like hypnotic state, the blades began to graze their naked chests. Mass hysteria affected the onlookers. Another doctor restrained Marion from rushing among them when it seemed as if at least one boy must inevitably commit ritual suicide. At the very last instant, two older boys leapt out of the crowd and stopped the young ones, who subsided in total exhaustion. Marion clutched her confrere's hand. The rescuers were actually attendants at the Denpasar hospital, training for medicine, but in the tenth-century Hindu ceremonial their appearance and personalities had altered beyond recognition.

In the course of our far-flung activities on the island four of our men made the rounds of the leper colonies where Dr. Reid, an Englishman, had been working for years. Bali has more than 2,000 lepers in five colonies fed by ninety-five clinics. A clinic may be simply a grass hut by the roadside or a station under a palm tree. Examiners carry equipment from one to the other in a pickup truck, including a bench to sit on while checking patients and a bucket of water to wash their hands.

One colony was on the edge of the sea, a lovely place, and each leper had his own grass hut. It was neat and clean and the inmates did their own work as they would have at home in their villages. There weren't as many cripples as we expected to see, though many had contractures of the hands, ulcers on their feet, or burns because the extremities were anesthetized by the disease and they felt no pain. UNICEF provides DDS (diphenylsulfone) given at the rate of 22 mgms. every three days and a nurse visits each clinic with supplies every two weeks. He finds the lepers waiting and examines them for any increase in lesions, any involvement of the nerves.

Lepers are supposed to live segregated in leprosaria, aloof from their families, but for festivals—such as the days on which the young boys participate in the kris ceremonial or young women "come out" by having their teeth filed—they go home. Many simply never return to the colonies. Sulfa is then prescribed for their near relatives, and when mothers have it, their babies are treated as well.

Did we do any real good as we fanned out over the island, joined by five Indonesian doctors from Djakarta, distributing drugs and vitamin-packed mixtures and passionate lectures against unnecessary ignorant carelessness? I think so. I know so. We *started* many things and furthered others. Sometimes people will listen to the stranger who arrives dramatically on a white horse or ship when they are deaf to their own wise men. And how recently were we in the U.S. subject to tuberculosis, smallpox, diphtheria, typhoid fever, and how long ago did we learn what vitamins and a balanced diet mean?

By being so flexible in our teaching, we could demonstrate the most complicated surgery and the use of the fly swatter during that same surgery. While we ate rice three times a day with them, varied only by cabbage for breakfast (which took more getting used to), fruit for lunch, and an occasional feast of turtle meat at night, we could preach the virtues of soybeans. Balinese physicians knew that tetanus was easily avoidable at birth, but *dukuns* and midwives had not learned to boil the scissors before they snipped umbilical cords. They welcomed us as guests and were happy to listen and heed.

Our Bali program went so well we sent a three-man team to Tabanan and Karangasem. And everywhere the response was what it had been in Denpasar. When we asked if they would carry on, they said, "Yes, indeed. We like it."

They liked us, too. "It is a happy feeling," said Dr. Djelantik before we left, "to be among friends whom we seemingly already knew a long time ago. I confess that before you came all of us were wondering how we would outlive an invasion of foreign doctors and nurses, until we suddenly got the idea that *we ourselves* are those who are to arrange things according to local needs. You appreciated us and our efforts in the midst of handicaps and limitations and we saw you at your work, taking notice of that specific western attitude to things-to-be-done, that striving for perfection in the performance of each piece of work. It was for that basic human feeling of friendship you and we so miraculously acquired from the first day on that I thank you the most. The help you gave us in the form of work, knowledge, experience, skill, and material is too much to sum up. The most lasting element you leave with us is the belief in the ability of mankind to make the human factor win over barriers laid by prejudices of race, politics, and paper bureaurocracy. Merry Christmas and a Happy New Year."

For the Balinese New Year on December 16 we had been royally entertained. President Sukarno and Pakistan's Mohammed Ayub Kahn were guests of honor and our section of the reviewing stand was next to theirs. The moment Sukarno saw us, he boomed, "Where's my nurse?" "His" nurse was Ruth Currie who had taken him through the *Hope* in Djakarta.

Finding her, he embraced her and kissed her on both cheeks.

His arrival signaled the start of a parade. Floats depicting Balinese life from birth to death went by in a riot of color. Banners and gamelan music accompanied dancers who pranced along the street.

That night at Sukarno's Balinese residence we were invited to a party, a dressy occasion for which most Hopies were unprepared. Jack Tetirick used a nurse's buttons for cuff links and everybody managed somehow. Dancers performed in an enclosure of palm and bamboo, Dr. Djelantik's daughter the loveliest of them all. Flowers were thrown to all the guests. President Sukarno turned around and gave his to Ann Roden.

After the fete, we went to work harder than ever. A few nights later, with only the barest of skeleton staffs on board, Ann Roden relieved another nurse at eight and a few minutes later a woman in the adult ward went abruptly into labor. The trouble for which she was admitted was well above the waist and no one had discovered the advanced pregnancy she carefully concealed. Ann was frightened to death. Not a single doctor was aboard. "Please, dear God," she prayed, "send someone back in time!"

Nurse-midwife Harriet Jordon arrived as the answer to prayer. The baby was delivered, the only newborn Hopie. Her father's name is I Madi Marija, her mother's Niketut Werta. The little Balinese girl's name is Jordon Hope.

Jordon Hope's parents came from a tiny hill town Nancy Campion visited. In a kampong she saw a woman making a piece of material, white with tones of red and blue, soft as feathers. She tried to buy it, but the weaver explained politely that it was not for sale. It had taken her three months to make it and it was to be her shroud. Later Father Magner brought the lovely stuff to Nancy. "She insisted on sending it with me," he said. "It's for you. She's decided to live another three months and wants you to have it."

For Christmas all the Americans came in from all over Bali to be "home." No mail had arrived from the U.S. and Christmas packages didn't reach us until February. The ship's shop was depleted because sailors found nylons better than cash as presents for ladies on shore. But Hopies had bargained in *pesars* (bazaars) on the island for wood carvings and trinkets. Names went into a hat and each was to give a present to the person whose name he drew.

On that brilliant sunny afternoon, we went swimming. The beaches at Denpasar were better, but the one in the cove was "ours." The children of Padangbai were so excited because we swam on the local beach at all—Americans never swam there and tourists rushed straight on to the capital—they had built us a beach house. The small hut was made of woven matting and palm leaves supported by heavy bamboo poles driven into the ground. A six-inch open space along the bottom let in the cool breezes. When they presented it, the oldest boy, spokesman for the swarm, announced, "I will be your houseboy. No one else may enter without your permission." It was a sweet memorial, like the Leaning Tower of Pisa we left behind later on Sumbawa.

Christmas night on board, the galley turned out a turkey dinner, very welcome after eating so long on shore. Dr. Dje-lantik sent us three Christmas trees, one for the staff and one for the crew and one, according to the custom of the sea, to be lashed to the mast. Decorations arrived from Hong Kong on a Java ferry we called "The African Queen" which usually carried chickens, pigs, goats, and crates of old automobile tires. Carols were sung from stem to stern and in the wards hung felt angels fashioned by Mary Finley.

At ten, Bill Anna held a Protestant service and at midnight Father Magner celebrated Mass in the classroom before an altar trimmed with tropical flowers and banked wih palm fronds from under the Southern Cross. Many Hopies went to both services.

The *Hope* was hooked up by radio-telephone to America and Nancy Campion was the first to speak to her mother, who urged her to wear the artics she had packed for Nancy's trip.

Santa Claus was a doctor in a red muu-muu and a mask digging packages from a potato sack. Captain Windas contributed a "box with a slot in the top" for Jordan Hope, but it was already too small for her. Dr. Spangler had made pop-corn and nurses commandeered the galley to turn out peanut brittle and fudge. At the eggnog party in the lounge, someone found a player piano roll of "Silent Night" and put it on.

We felt close to each other and far from America and still uncertain. Bali was an experience that would take digesting. We were deeply touched by the warmth, the humility, and the pride of Dr. Djelantik's farewell and the "precious achievement of friendship" but we hadn't yet the oneness and sure sense of mission that came with the overwhelming experiences of Sumbawa and Makassar and Ambon and Kupang and Sumbawa again. We were, though, readier than we had been.

Alex Sahagian-Edwards, who would rise so well to the sight that confronted us in Sumbawa, Pesar's palace pesthouse, seemed more or less prepared for anything at all.

Just before *Hope*'s sailing day, he went out in the Captain's gig with two engineers and a dozen staffers. The splendor of the sun disappeared behind sudden black clouds and a downpour was followed by fog so thick they could not find the ship. "Never mind," said Alex, "we'll just sail on to Sumbawa and tell them we're the *Hope*."

Chapter XVI

The Hope sailed on from Paradise Lost to Sumbawa to become—through trial and triumph—a strong, unshatterable working realization of the HOPE dream. If we never achieved our own perfect ideal, we who believed in HOPE and who worked for it could, from then on, be proud and certain of its worth.

At the same time, under pressure from our eastern hosts, Project HOPE undertook several antic ventures. We were urged to send missions away from the ship, far into the field, to places where no Americans had ever been before and to one no white man had yet been.

What the permanent value of these missions was I don't know. We made new and strange friends—but we made friends everywhere. Certainly we could not do much teaching

under conditions that made Sumbawa seem civilized, but we
did bring back intimate medical knowledge of territory un-
charted even by the Indonesian Ministry of Health. They
would use this information in making their future plans. The
local *panitya*, who had their hearts set on getting attention
from us, considered that the more patients we saw the more
successful we were. On that basis, our achievements in these
out-of-the-way places were staggering.

The most revealing reports came directly and privately
to me from the men we sent. I hope I do not violate
their confidential nature by quoting from them. Two of our
most invaluable doctors, HOPE's admitting officer Yates and
rotator-surgeon Goiney, insisted on going out—and we insisted
that they carry special radio equipment to keep in touch with
us as well as to file personal reports. Nobody knew what
might happen.

Jim Yates had already practiced medicine in Indonesia
from 1953 to 1955. He understood and spoke the language and
was familiar with the needs and customs of the people. Can-
nibalism, he informed us happily, was still a tribal custom in
some of the wilder sections to which we were sending him.
But "only ceremonially." What that seemed to mean was that
nothing human was eaten except the fingers, tongue, and
heart.

Dr. Bernard J. Goiney of Seattle, Washington, had joined
us in Makassar but not because he had romantic illusions
about tropical islands. "The travel folders don't fool me.
I've been there," he said. For two and a half years he had
served with the Navy ship *Mercy* in New Guinea, the Philip-
pines, Okinawa, and Korea. He liked mission HOPE better
than mission *Mercy*. "During the war we were doing traumatic
surgery. We would have as many as thirty deaths on a
mission. The work we're doing here now is reconstructive.
There's a lot of satisfaction in that and in training people
to help themselves." Stateside his specialty was gynecological
surgery but he could turn his skillful hand to any part of the
anatomy. "I love these people," the deeply tanned, blue-eyed
man admitted. "They don't thank you in words but one of
them will grab your hand and give it a little squeeze."

Our team was heading into the Moluccas, the Spice Islands of history, spread to the north close beside the farthest western islands of New Guinea. To take them there, a squat and dumpy over-age island steamer *Babut* stood offshore at Ambon when the *Hope* anchored there.

The *Babut* wasn't more than a hundred feet over-all. Mavis Pate packed sterile instruments for Goiney suitable for all surgical procedures except lung and brain operations. We couldn't send proper anesthetics for those. Claire O'Neil oversaw the large shipment of powdered milk and drugs. There wouldn't be much room to spare for Goiney, Yates, Stanley Hellman, a young dentist from Chicago, and Charles Dickerson, Michigan pharmacist, let alone the ten Indonesians who made up our group, and we were dismayed when we noticed Ambonese piling aboard the *Babut*, bringing with them mats, cookstoves, bamboo furniture, ducks, geese, chickens, parrots, goats, a monkey, and a deer.

The *Hope* registered a polite protest but was equally politely rebuffed by the *Babut*. Boats toured the islands so infrequently that these people had waited months, even years, to get onto one. If the *Babut* was going anywhere, they were going, too.

After working all day without time for lunch in Ambon, Goiney and company went aboard. Yates made the first entries in the daily log.

February 16, 1961
    No supper. Just as well for our waistlines, though Mr. Dickerson would get lost if he got any thinner. Evening passed playing an Indonesian card game resembling dominoes. All turned in early, tired from hauling supplies in the intense heat. No blankets and no sheets so froze during the night. Event of the evening was when Hellman, for some reason, sprayed the pantry. By rough estimate a million cockroaches came out of hiding to infest the whole ship. Night was peaceful and sea smooth but the quiet was marred by some jackass repeatedly whistling "What a Friend we have in Jesus." That, and the clang of bells and the cold kept us from getting much sleep. It was resolved to devote the following day to tracking down the Whistler.

February 17, 1961
    Arrived at Namlea, Buru in Malaku Tengah at 6 A.M.

Radioed *Hope:* TODAY: 112 PRESCRIPTIONS FILLED 60 OUT-
PATIENTS SEEN 8:00–12: NOON 20 OUTPATIENTS SEEN 1:00–
4:00 P.M. 20 INPATIENTS SEEN IN MALE WARD 6 INPATIENTS
SEEN IN FEMALE WARD 61 DENTAL PATIENTS ATTENDED BY
DR. HELLMAN WHO REPORTED THAT ALL HIS PATIENTS GOT
ASPIRIN, SOME GOT PENICILLIN BUT ALL GOT AMERICAN OBAT
(medicine).

On this island we saw many eye cases, mostly blind, much
anemia, ancylostoma plus malaria, TB, parasites, yaws, and
elephantiasis. Namlea, principal city of the Isle of Buru, 4,000
out of 8,000 total population, mostly Christian. The clinic has
about thirty-five beds and

4 mandris—attendants with six years of grammar school,
some job training, and
No doctors
1 midwife
1 laboratory technician
No X ray
No surgery

Hellman's personal *Klinik Gigi,* dental clinic, for the day
was a wall. Ten people at a time lined up. They all had such
lamentable teeth that he could do few fillings. Injecting them
from left to right with Novacain, he then went back and
pulled from left to right. Teeth were strewn the length of the
wall. One boy who backed up against a glass window went
through the pane into the room where Yates was examining a
patient but his bad tooth remained outside in Hellman's firm
grip.

That night food supplies put aboard the *Babut* from the
Hope were investigated. They turned out to consist of a box
of crackers, a bottle of ketchup, a jar of peanut butter, cans of
pineapple, and instant coffee. ("We needed that pineapple
like a hole in the head," snorted Goiney later. Fresh fruit
including pineapples and delicious mangosteens grow everywhere.) It had been understood by everybody except the
Babut's Captain that he would feed them. The Captain said
he supposed Americans would do anything rather than eat
Indonesian food. However, he invited them to dinner the
following night.

Log, February 18, 1961
Arrived at island of Batjan, town of Labuha, 10 A.M. Radioed
Hope. The one doctor is Kwee, a former colleague of mine in

Surabaja. Note that he was paid more as a mandri in my clinic
when he was still a student than he gets here now as a government physician.

Functioning at local polyclinic by 10:30.

Saw 113 patients. Goiney scheduled a hydrocele, 1 hernia.
Nurses held flashlights so he could finish. 2nd hydrocele can-
celed because no light.

Hellman saw 62 patients with Dr. Lehm. 84 extractions,
4 fillings.

Didn't go to hospital.

Dr. Kwee's hospital had twenty beds but it was eight kilometers from town on a high knoll. When the government
built it in 1955 the site was selected because it was healthy
and it was planned to move the whole village there. The
villagers stayed stubbornly where they were in spite of mud
and malaria. When Kwee's very small ration of official gasoline
ran out he had to walk back and forth. Hellman, chatting
with the town kids, asked about an abandoned horsecart. The
only horse on the island, they told him, was *sudah mati*,
already dead.

At the Captain's dinner that night, three bowls were put on
the table. Taking their cue from the Indonesians, the Americans helped themselves to rice, next to a soupy green vegetable and finally to something that resembled canned dead
horse. Then they took a generous bite of the mixture. It exploded in their mouths like TNT. They could not breathe or
speak and tears streamed down their faces. However, one
bite proved anesthetic. After a minute they could taste nothing at all so they went on eating.

Log, February 19, 1961

Left Labuha at 6 A.M. Additional passenger one large turtle.
Installed in head. Smooth sea, fabulously beautiful islands
with dense green foliage. Many coasts lined with palm trees.
Coming up to Ternate are six islands in a row, all beautiful,
all are extinct volcanoes and all growing coconuts.

Ternate at 4 P.M. Committee which met us included the
Mayor, the head of the Public Service, Dr. Bone of the
Army, and Dr. Tan, head of government medical service.
Radioed *Hope*. After coffee at the Mayor's we were taken
to see the Rajah's palace and the hospital.

The palace was an immense white building on the green

flank of the volcano overlooking the harbor. Regal steps wound up to the veranda. At the top of the steps they found the door open and entered a sweeping hall, half again as long as the *Babut*. The room contained exactly two objects: a crystal chandelier with wilting candles in its sockets and a large Ming vase. Through a distant door the Rajah's son came in ceremonial dress to greet them. He was young, handsome, and spoke flawless English. After amenities were exchanged, Yates asked if he would inherit the title. "No," he said. "My father is the last Rajah. We are becoming modern. There will be no more Rajahs here."

On that strange, orchid-shaped island of Halamahera, the most modern thing was the hospital in Ternate. It had fifty beds, an apothecary, an operating room, and one Catholic Sister who had it well organized, clean, and efficient. She told our hosts the clinic would be open for the Americans in the morning and Goiney discussed the scheduling of operations for the afternoon.

Unfortunately the Mayor insisted that our doctors stay with him that night instead of on the *Babut*, out on the water. Goiney found himself in a large room with an immense iron bedstead, wrought in an elaborate pattern of hearts and swathed in a muslin canopy. The bridal suite, he thought. Thank God, no bride, and thank heaven a mosquito net. He crawled inside it and fell asleep. Two hours later he waked up, embattled. Hordes of mosquitoes had found a victim—one Bernard J. Goiney. His flashlight showed a mass of rips in the netting.

With about three hours' sleep "whether we needed it or not" and covered with bites, the medical staff went on duty in the morning. The hospital was fine, but neither Dr. Tan nor the police could keep order. People poured down from the mountains for American *obat*. The crowd became so large and insistent that Dr. Tan and the chief of police insisted on closing the clinic at 3:15. After that Yates helped Goiney as his anesthetist while Dr. Ong assisted. In the slight cool of the evening the Mayor's guests were taken to dance at the best and only hotel in town.

Before they said good night they asked again if there had

been any radio messages from the *Hope* in reply to theirs.
There were none.

> Log, February 21, 1961
> Left Ternate at 6 A.M., arrived Tidore at 7:30 A.M.
> Village of Sasiu is home of Oesman Amirrudin, one of our
> Indonesian male nurses.
> From boat to house of Governor of Indonesian New Guinea.
> Then got the one doctor, Piati, out of bed. He's had malaria.
> Clinic 9:30 A.M. to 1:30 P.M., 2:30 P.M. to 4 P.M.
> Number of patients seen (2 American, 2 Indonesian doctors)
> —175
> Dental—42
> Saw quite a bit of obesity on the island, something I have
> noticed in the Maluccas, though very seldom in Java.
> Remaining medical supplies given to Dr. Piati.
> Visited Amiruddin's family in the evening. He is the big
> hero of the village for having brought project HOPE to them.
> Spoke English to him so he could show off his.
> No word from *Hope*. Are we abandoned?
> Left Tidore 8 P.M. Everybody seasick except Goiney and
> Hellman.

Instead of hugging the islands on the trip home the *Babut*
headed on a straight run of thirty-six hours across the open
sea. The area, as someone mentioned later, is the delivery
room for hurricanes.

Goiney prided himself on his immunity to seasickness. He
had crossed the equator thirty-three times without a qualm.
This time only *mabuk laut*, a lightning attack of Indonesian
dysentery, saved him. It served as a counterirritant. Springing
from bunk to head he found the turtle capsized and sliding
from bulkhead to bulkhead on its back every time the boat
lurched. To dodge the creature Goiney did a bizarre dance.
"Kept my mind off my troubles," he admitted. As for Hellman,
Goiney commented, "He was so euphoric over all those teeth
he didn't have the sense to be seasick."

The *Hope's* whistle sounded loud and welcome when the
Babut finally lurched into Ambon harbor. It seemed mighty
good to be "home."

"Where have you been?" demanded Mavis Pate. "You
promised to let us hear from you!"

Two weeks later the first radio message from Namlea was filed in the radio shack on the *Hope*'s top deck.

"We might have been eaten by cannibals," said Jim Yates cheerfully, "and you wouldn't have known it till Easter."

Irrepressibly he had set off almost at once on the second trip out of Ambon to Saparua, Amahai, Mauku, and into Ceram's aboriginal country. For five nights Yates, Benner, Hanan, Hellman, Dickerson, and two Indonesian male nurses were aboard the island-hopper. This time they slept on deck in stretchers, sarongs wrapped around their shoulders. The heat, close in to land, was oppressive.

Kepala Pemerinta, regional executive administrator of public health, met them in Saparua. Their first tour was to see the local leprosarium, and the first surgery included the amputation of a leprous ulcerated foot. No Ciba 1906, the wonder drug that had closed leprosariums in many less afflicted lands, had yet reached there.

That night, at dinner in Kepala Pemerinta's home, the *Hope*'s party were introduced to "everyone," including the local schoolteachers. After Yates made a short, appreciative speech thanking them for such a welcome, they all stood in a circle and joined in the famous and moving Ambonese song of farewell.

> *Siok, mari pulang pulang, temon é*
> *La bintang siang bintang siang la sudah naik*
> *Siok mari pulang mail pulang temon é*
> *Le bintang siang bintang siang la sudah masuk.*

Log, February 29, 1961

Morning well organized. Dr. Tjong personally screened more than 500 patients so that we saw only the sick cookies we could help with American *obat*. Interesting cases: leprosy, pyelonephritis, trachoma, elephantiasis.

The officials of the city were invited to dine with us aboard the *Babut* our last evening in Saparua. Chef: S. M. Hellman, DDS.

MENU

Chilled California Tomato Juice Supreme with Sodium Benzoate

Genuine Imported American mouse cheese, with acidus citricus

Imported NBC Sno-flake Premium Crackers (#2)

Steak, Bone, T, à la Hellman, Black Angus Steer, Champion
Chicago Stockyards, 1934
Nasih Putih
Tomatoes, lettuce hearts, sauce à Le Leper
Bread direct from Kapal _Hope_ bakeries with New Zealand
green valley butter
Choice of fruits
Coffee, tea, milk, or Gula with Ants
Liquor: Porto Saparua
Bed before twelve, off to Amahai around 5:30 A.M.
Left behind 25,000 tablets of Ciba 1906 for pilot study in
leprosy control.

March 1, the expedition arrived in Amahai, the first Americans ever to land there. The inhabitants were pro-Dutch,
pro-white, and anti-Java, and not only presented themselves
for treatment with alacrity but gave an official ball for their
visitors. "People vary so much from one island to another,"
commented Hanan, "and are so marked in their differences,
it is almost impossible to regard it as one country and one
people."

Strangest of all was the village of Sepa in Ceram Tengah.
No white man had appeared before in the area. "Millions" of
curious kids, who ducked if the palefaces came close, turned
out to stare and so did red-turbaned Hindus, from aborigine
stock, with black fuzzy hair parted down the middle. The
chief proudly displayed his village of bamboo houses and
explained that pregnant or menstruating women were banished
to shacks behind the houses where no man could enter. For
the benefit of our camera addicts, he lined up his people to
be photographed and the young men climbed the coconut
trees and dropped coconuts down for the visitors to drink the
fresh milk.

Jim came back with a gift of arrows made of slivers of
bamboo, some poisoned and some not. The unpoisoned ones
were for hunting animals, the poisoned ones for people. Since
all of our people survived all of these trips with their fingers,
tongues, and hearts intact, we must conclude that HOPE and
its representatives were welcome—any time, anywhere, under
almost any circumstances.

Chapter XVII

In fact, the more our reputation grew and the more popular we became, the more the Indonesians would have liked to keep us around. Since our trip would end, of necessity, in less than a year, they began to ask what we could do about assigning individuals to them on a more permanent basis.

Back in Djakarta, Minister Satrio told me he wanted help in opening a new portion of the Ibu Sukarno Hospital. Could we send them a team to help in setting up the orthopedic wing? I answered with a glib yes, thinking that the Oriental pace of things would leave me with six months to get somebody.

"Fine," said Satrio. "We'll be ready in three weeks."

Your word is your bond with this man and if I couldn't get a team ready I had to find at least one outstanding doctor. Henry Emmel of the Seattle Orthopedic Clinic was a stalwart supporter. The day after I telephoned him in the U.S. he called me back. Seattle's Dr. John LeCocq, founder of the clinic, would come for four months. I confess I did not realize then what a man I was getting. Dr. John is one of the fathers of modern orthopedic surgery in the Northwest, an impressive, white-haired fellow with a puckish look and a sturdy character.

Certain advisors thought he might be too forthright for an Oriental country, but it turned out that he made more friends than almost anybody. His popular nickname became "Dr. No Sugar." This referred to his refreshing candor, his downright disposition, and his determined efforts to prevent Indonesians from imbibing their favorite soft drinks. Orange crush, he said, was too sweet and bad for them. Not only did he sweep aside red tape and ignore confusion, but he commandeered all the instruments he needed, some from the *Hope* and the rest from friends back home.

When he met Sukarno, John spoke Dutch which delighted

the President. Laughing, Sukarno warned LeCocq, "Just don't speak it around town, or these people will shoot you."

"Nonsense," said John. "You shouldn't pay attention to such things, but spend more money for health and hospitals."

Before LeCocq went home, he brought Dr. Henry Nash and pretty Irish nurse Marjorie McQuillan out from the Seattle Clinic to take over. Later they were joined by Thomas Angland, orthopedist (and leading Rotarian) from Yakima, Washington.

Polio is not a major problem there, but it is endemic and the effects are worsened by the Asian habit of squatting. One patient of Angland's could ambulate by holding her feet and leaping, rather like a frog, but her legs were bent double. It took infinite pains and care to straighten her up. Dr. Angland used her as an example when he talked to the Rotary Club in Djakarta of which he became an active member. Through Angland, the Djakarta Rotarians began to take an active interest in the work with crippled children at Ibu Sukarno. A large portrait of sixty-four-year-old "Dr. No Sugar," who set a record for difficult operations while he was there, hangs on the wall.

We also arranged for a few men to undertake special, long-term missions in the islands. Two of these were Dr. Max Hirschfelder, ophthalmologist from Centralia, Illinois, and Stanley Mayall, DDS, of Spokane, Washington. They spent the winter and spring on Bali, working with the local men at the Sanglah Hospital in Denpasar.

Mayall had been with us on the *Hope* and Hirschfelder had informed Project HOPE in the States, "Have ophthalmoscope, will travel."

When Hirschfelder reached Bali he found the local and only ophthalmologist, Jurnjakob Diehn. Diehn was under contract to the Indonesian government. Meeting on the island the two eye doctors discovered that they had more than a profession in common. They were both German refugees. Hirschfelder had come to Centralia from Munich in 1936. After World War II, Diehn found that his home was in Communist East Germany and he left for Indonesia.

Together, communicating easily in their native German, they

coped with one disease Hirschfelder had never seen before.
Diehn called it "rice-field keratitis," a virus infection of the
fields. And together they performed so many operations on
patients that Hirschfelder lost count in his first week. To
escape blindness, so dreadfully prevalent in this beautiful
place, people came to them from as far as six days away by
prahu.

Hirschfelder's main recurrent problem was his raiment.
His borrowed surgical suits, changed often in the tropically
hot operating room, were made for Indonesian bodies and he
was well over six feet tall. Sometimes he stretched right out
of the seat of the trousers, sending the Indonesian nurses into
hysterics. Finally one was assigned the job of keeping Dr. H.
in one piece.

He never let this interfere with his work or his philosophy.
"You can't buy friendship with money," said Dr. Hirschfelder.
"You can only buy it with friendship. For the man who has
nothing, like these people on Bali, the little Communism offers—a broad general mediocrity—seems like paradise. Only
by personal contacts like these can we show him that there
is something beyond mediocrity and that it is possible for him
to attain it. HOPE brings human beings to human beings."

I guess in the end it always comes down to that—human
being to human being, individuals and their lives, individual
doctors, patients, nurses, Americans, Indonesians, children,
adults. . . .

Your heart not only goes out to people, the separate people,
who are helped by a cause, but also to those who serve it. I
will always feel that Nurse Lois Boyce gave her life for HOPE,
though she might indeed have died if she had never come
with us.

Lois's story belongs in the story of HOPE. And in her
memory, I will tell it.

Chapter XVIII

Thursday, February 23, began normally enough. After breakfast outpatient clinic people headed for the gig, led by Norton
Benner. A step or two behind was Jim Yates, wearing his
perpetual expression of being on the verge of a great new
experience, and Arnold Smoller, placidly composed. Richard
Elliott trailed with three of the nurses, Bettie Ahern, Dottie
Rivera, and Lottie Reich. They were going to work in the
town of Ambon.

Routine was in full swing aboard the ship where Mavis
Pate was directing her charges and the operating room. Surgeons Walt Haynes from Columbus and Hank Bodner of Los
Angeles knew Mavis was the boss. Our Indonesian anesthetist,
Lieutenant F. W. Ferdinandus, was at his post. He had been
in training since Djakarta and was already so proficient he
was insulting our surgeons, frequently the trademark of a good
anesthetist. Ambon was home for him though he had been
away for fifteen years and had not yet seen his parents. A
few days earlier they had watched him doing his job over
the ship's TV. Ferdinandus was still walking on air. Hugh
Jordan, a rotator in anesthesia, had just arrived and was
momentarily in the position of being an observer—of Ferdinandus.

On the admitting deck, white-haired, monkish Tim Lally
readied his Picker unit for another day of mass chest X rays.

It was a day like any other except for one thing. In the
women's ward a thirty-two-year-old laboratory technician,
Lois Boyce, lay gravely ill. Lois, a willowy, fair-haired girl
from Minnesota, had gentle ways, ready humor, and an en-
dearingly sweet smile. She was one of the most popular girls
aboard. On and off for weeks she had been bothered by headaches over one eye. She complained very little but I wonder
now whether she wouldn't have taken to her bed if she had
been working in an ordinary hospital.

When Lois began having dizzy spells every time she stood up her devoted roommates turned her in to the doctors. Specialists of all types examined her and made no positive findings of anything serious.

However Mark Beaubien, then senior medical officer, was alarmed and put her to bed for concentrated observation. That morning Lois vomited. The nurse on duty called Mark who, heartsick, began to suspect that she might have a brain tumor. There weren't more than five or six different sorts of illness that we could not handle at that time. Brain tumor was one of them.

Everything was checked again—the headaches were not constant but came and went starting as dull pain and accelerating rapidly if she got up. Worse, she could no longer sit up in comfort. Mark called for two sets of skull X rays, then asked staff specialists to observe her eye grounds.

They found nothing specific but he remained troubled. "I can't pinpoint it," he told his colleagues, "but somehow I sense a slight change. One of Lois' roommates has told me that she seems a little different. Nothing startling, but not like herself. She thought it was just on account of the headaches. Now, with the vomiting, I'm afraid there may be a lesion."

"Heavenly God," said one of the physicians, "if you're right, what can we do for her?" (At that time we did not carry a neurosurgeon.)

"It's a cinch we can't help her here," said Mark soberly, "and there's no plane due for two weeks. We've got to find a way to get her out of here, and fast."

Within five minutes the group convened in Beaubien's cabin with Captain Gerber to lay plans.

"Let's radio the Chief of Naval Operations in Washington," Gerber suggested. "We'll try to raise Djakarta, too." The ham radio station aboard the SS *Hope* went into action. Fortunately we could reach Washington more easily than Djakarta thanks to one Bill Green in San Francisco, our blessed year-long link with home. He called Steve Alex at the Project's Washington office and Steve called Jim Bell in the State Department and Arleigh Burke, Chief of Naval Operations. All that night Bell stayed at his desk trying to get through to Djakarta and

Burke did, too. Between them they reached American Ambassador Howard Jones at last. It was the long way round but things were beginning to tick.

Colonel Henry McCartney, Jones' naval attaché, reminded the Ambassador that according to regulations it would take three days to get the Indonesian Air Force to approve an unscheduled flight like the one he proposed.

"Tell them this is different, Mac," said Ambassador Jones. "Tell them this is to save the life of an American citizen who came here to help them. They'll understand that. They all remember what the HOPE people did to try to save just one Indonesian girl here."

McCartney cleared red tape with the Air Force as if cutting it with a scalpel. What was supposed to take three days took three hours. We weren't in the clear though. The nearest place to Ambon where there was probably a neurosurgeon and a neurologist was Clark Air Force Base Hospital in Manila, a couple of thousand miles away.

I was not in Ambon but in Djakarta arranging for the *Hope*'s return there when the message came in. Permission was granted for me to go with the plane which would leave at nine that night and fly nonstop to Ambon, provided the fuel held out. The old R-4D, Navy version of the Dakota, had a cruising speed of 150 knots and, with a following wind and no bad breaks, might make it direct, thereby saving a good hour. At my request the Ambassador was letting Guy Kirkendall, a master of many Indonesian dialects, come with us. If we had to come down in some God-forsaken spot, we were going to need him to translate.

Guy promptly got into the act and performed miracles. Regulations called for exit visas, Philippine visas, and, to be on the safe side, Japanese visas. In two and a half hours, thanks to him and Dorothy Broussard of the Embassy, we acquired clearances that were normally not forthcoming in less than three days.

By eight we were at the airport. On the large field the lonely R-4D with an American flag painted on the fuselage was being serviced. As we watched, a fire broke out in the starboard engine. Well, I thought, here goes the ball game.

McCartney didn't turn a hair. Fuel, he explained composedly, had spilled over onto the engine cowling. The flames were quickly doused. Looking very natty in an orange flight suit, McCartney taxied us down the runway at nine o'clock precisely. Jack Davey, the Navy staff doctor there to assume technical responsibility for a patient on a Navy plane, Guy, and I strapped our seat belts and settled down.

It had been a hard day. I had skirted a crowd of Communist Lumumba demonstrators in the morning, held an exhausting conference with an Indonesian politician and a second one to repair any damage the first conference might have done, before I received the terrible news of Lois' illness. Worn out, I slept until, nearly nine hours later, McCartney circled the field at Ambon.

Dawn was breaking over the jungle that girdled the bay. The radio watch was, apparently, wrapped in slumber as deep as mine had been, for we continued to circle for an hour and a half before we could rouse him. The interval of waiting was brightened by a heartening sight, the good ship *Hope*. When we were released from our suspension in space and taxied down the field, children sprang up like weeds out of the ground and surrounded the plane. A few security guards sauntered up and then the field's commanding officer marched briskly into view and Colonel McCartney, U.S.N., saluted smartly. The officer was an old friend with whom I had flown from Ambon to Djakarta when I made my survey trip the previous year. We greeted one another warmly. "How," I asked, "is the *Hope* ship doing?"

He was delighted with her. Yesterday he had had his back X-rayed aboard and today his wife and one of their children were to be patients. McCartney broke in on this recital. "Captain," he said, "can I get gas?"

"How much do you need?" my Indonesian friend inquired.

"If you could fill her up," Mac said, "I could fly straight through to Manila but they told me at headquarters you could only spare 600 gallons."

"Take all you need, Colonel," said my generous friend. "We owe it to you."

The next thing we needed was transportation to the dock.

Easy, he said. The ride would take about an hour and a half and we could leave as soon as he went home and washed up, in about fifteen minutes, he assured me. I sighed. Knowing the tempo of his part of the world I prepared to wait at least an hour. But he was back in twenty minutes. "Would you mind to wait," he said, dashing my hopes of getting away promptly, "another fifteen minutes? My wife and boy are getting dressed. They will ride with us."

At last a small wartime jeep with a cracked windshield, dilapidated canvas top, and dented fenders drew up. Said the Captain: "Would you mind to wait another fifteen minutes? I must get gasoline for the jeep."

It all took an hour, as I'd known it would, before we piled the Captain's very pregnant wife and his son into the back seat. We were cramped. Perhaps, he suggested, he should go ahead alone and see if he could not get a boat to send for us. That was more than my nerves could stand.

"Captain," I said, "if your wife can make the trip we can. Please let's go."

We were quite a sight scrunched into the oldest jeep I have ever seen. The clutch slipped, the horn sounded only when the Captain relinquished the wheel and made contact between two wires dangling from the steering shaft. As we turned off the airfield I saw a beat-up sign that read: "Ambon, 35 Kms."

The road was a muddy trail with rocks strewn haphazardly to provide a surface. We bumped and sank into potholes under foreboding trees at a racy twenty miles an hour. The air was moist with little sunlight breaking through, the sounds exotic. Strange birds called and an occasional falling tree cracked the stillness like a whip. Small groups of houses dotted the road-side and children, barefoot but cleanly dressed, bound for school and each carrying a book, ducked out of our way, laughing and shouting: "Hopie! Hopie!" That familiar sound, the way they used our name, cheered me.

No one talked but the Captain. His wife, he told us with some pride, was expecting her tenth child and planned to have more. We only hoped she wouldn't produce the tenth then and there. He owned a farm and the more hands he had the more food he could grow. Big families were the thing, there was plenty of land.

We progressed, over and through streams swollen by the rainy season, where women washed themselves or their clothes and children gamboled around them. We steered around and over landslides and crossed gullies on boards, the Captain clinging to the gearshift to keep the engine in second. Wild pigs fled before the uproar of our motor. After some twenty-five kilometers we emerged onto a paved road. Ambon was near now.

As we approached it, there were streamers suspended over our heads. I groaned. Probably more of the "Long Live Lumumba," "Recognize the Gizenga Government," "Convene the Congolese Parliament," stuff I thought. The Commies were hammering away everywhere.

"Look at that," said Guy, removing his pipe from between his teeth. "It says 'Hope represents the heart of America.' And that one is 'Hope is here for the sake of Humanity.'"

At the dock we were stopped by a guard standing beneath a sign: Hope. Already several hundred people were lined up along the quay, some waiting for the shore outpatient clinic, others for launches to take them aboard.

No boat was scheduled to go out until nine o'clock but Benner & Co. were ahead of schedule. The team came in view even while we were wangling transportation from the harbor master and, after I had had a few words with my compatriots, we set out for the *Hope* along with the first load of patients.

Jim Enright met me at the gangway. He had had no inkling that I was coming. After a short consultation with others of the staff, Mark Beaubien and I went to Lois' cabin.

Her face was wan and flower-like but her "hello" hearty.

"Why on earth are you doing all this for me, Dr. Walsh?" she inquired when I told her that we wanted to get her to Manila. "It makes me feel silly. I'm sure there's nothing seriously wrong."

I said the only thing I could say, that she was probably right but we wanted to be sure.

"Oh, gosh," said our good American Lois.

I smiled numbly at Harriet Siepel and Ginny Fernbach who

had begun packing for Lois without hesitation as soon as they heard what I had to say. Ann Roden was standing by to do what she could.

"I've been feeling ever so much better the last couple of days," Lois said, "and I hate to leave." I patted her hand and Mark and I left the cabin and called the staff together. I had a message for them from President Kennedy.

To all who participated in the mission of the HOPE he sent congratulations for the excellent work they were doing, in demonstrating the desire of Americans to share their scientific advances with other peoples. Senator Humphrey, too, commended them for their services to humanity.

So far away and so splendidly remembered! They were obviously tired but the words, coupled with my promise that there would be a ten-day vacation before we reached Saigon, lifted spirits.

A ship's officer notified me that McCartney was ready and so was Lois. As we went down the side the rails were lined with Hopies. I embraced as many as I could. I wanted to hug them all.

Below, Lois lay on a stretcher, wearing a silly straw hat with red daisies and a monkey on the brim, ringed round by her dearest friends who had asked to be allowed to go to the airfield: Priscilla Strong, Claire O'Neil, Maria Digges, a medical secretary, and others. Lois smiled contentedly. There was gaiety on the ride across the bay, forced but successful. Lois giggled at every sally.

At the dock we loaded our patient and ourselves into an Indonesian army truck, then promptly unloaded ourselves when we found the engine was dead. Fiddling with it proved fruitless, so willing shoulders pushed the lorry for a short distance and the motor caught.

It was Friday noon. I reached up to my face and realized that I had not shaved since Thursday morning.

No one could be comfortable on that terrible drive but when we reached the plane we got Lois into a bunk up forward and took to our own seats as the "No smoking—Fasten seat belts" sign flashed on. It was an outwardly uneventful flight. Lois did not seem ill and, like us, ate the sandwiches

Lois Boyce undertook her tasks as medical technician with an unwavering devotion that ended only with her death

Everywhere we set up clinics inquisitive heads appeared in windows to inspect marvels like Florence Mudge's microscope

Captain Gerber radios instructions to shore hospital for Dr. Bernard J. Goiney and therapist Sue Glocke

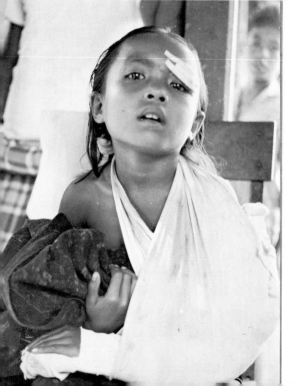

On earthquake - shaken Flores, a small girl accepts HOPE ministrations stoically

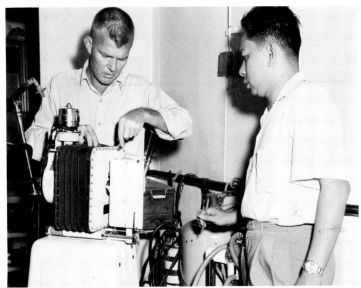

Leo Haney could fix anything from a Pulmotor to a cranky radio.
He was in constant demand

Doctors, nurses, and students follow an operation broadcast to the
classroom and explained by Dr. Misuraca

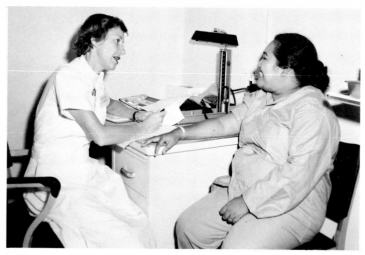

Dr. Glover and overweight patient

To prevent future epidemics, sanitary engineer Richard Mark analyzed local water and instituted purification system

Teresa Campbell sweetens a lesson on folding surgical sheets with a smile. Male outnumber female nurses in the Orient

On Flores Island, HOPE doctors did all they could to lighten the local doctor's heavy case load. Dr. Marion Wier examines baby

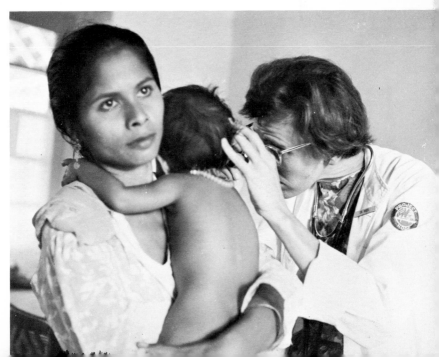

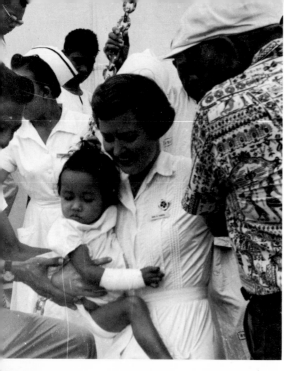

Ruth Currie returns a young charge with a bandaged arm to her delighted and grateful father

Dr. Robert Pulliam had a way with him that made grownups invite him in and droves of urchins follow him around

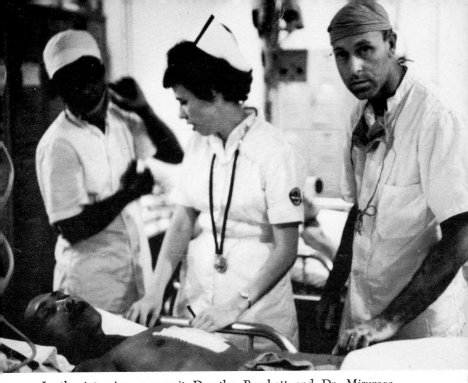

In the intensive care unit Dorothy Burchett and Dr. Misuraca
check post-operative condition of patient receiving transfusion

At the request of the Indonesian government, HOPE's Dr. John
LeCocq set up a permanent program, to be carried on by Dr. Sjarif
Thajeb, and manned by HOPE-trained personnel

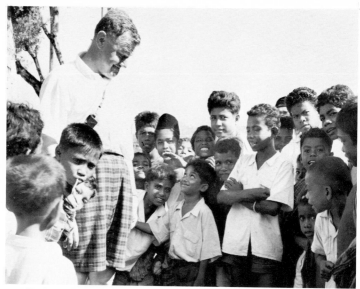

Small, but cheeky Indonesian boy gives Dr. McCannel his hand

The entire youthful population of Flores Island swarmed onto and
leapt off the dock to cheer the *Hope* when she sailed

steward McGorian had prepared and talked intermittently. A dark tropical night descended as we passed over the tip of Luzon. At ten the plane came down on an airstrip marked by the flashing red light of an ambulance.

An anxious, waiting photographer snapped a picture of Lois as she walked, smiling, off the plane. It would never do for a sob-sister story.

Kirkendall and I were exhausted, and now that Lois was in competent hands we slid off into two rooms that had been found for us in the hospitals' orthopedic ward. At seven the next morning a Filipino hospital attendant called us, saying that Colonel Burke, executive officer of the hospital, would like to meet us for breakfast. Then everything piled up fast.

Tom Wilson, a darkly handsome young medic, gave it to us straight as we gulped coffee. A left frontal lobe tumor. Left optic disc beginning to fill. And then the absolute hell— "We simply have no neurological facilities here."

"Where, then?" I heard my voice coming from a long way off.

"Tachikawa Air Force Hospital in Tokyo. Best hope," he said and I knew it was no hope.

I turned to the colonel. "What chance is there of getting through?" I asked.

"No question of chance," he said. "We'll find an airplane somewhere and get here there. Tom, alert nurse Mary Warner. We'll give you a set of invitation orders, Dr. Walsh. But what about Mr. Kirkendall?"

"Guy wants to get back to Djakarta," I said, "so don't worry about him."

The colonel exploded into action. Sitting in his office I heard him attack every angle. The complication was that an air exercise, "Operation Long Pass," was just ending and all planes were tied up. He was dogged and at the end of a couple of hours looked up with immense relief.

"Got it," he said. "A C-130 just in from Bangkok. It can be ready in an hour and a half. Ought to make the 2,000 miles to Tokyo in five hours. It means bumping a general and his helicopter they were taking to Kadena Air Base at Okinawa."

"Won't he mind?" I marveled.

"No," said the wise colonel. "The higher they are, the more understanding. Get ready. We'll pick you and your luggage up in a truck and Tom Wilson will bring Miss Boyce and a nurse along in an ambulance. I'll work on your orders and the sergeant will deliver them to the plane."

"Right, sir," I said and damn near saluted.

The plane we had taken over was a big C-130 with an orange nose, a four-engine propjet cargo and troop carrier. Her tail section was open and it was vast enough to carry many men and vehicles. Lois lay awaiting in her ambulance, saying over and over, "What a lot of trouble you're going to for me."

Nurse Warner, a trim figure in her Air Force blue uniform, was small, pert, hiding her charm behind efficient spectacles, and kindly. All her energy was concentrated on making Lois comfortable and happy.

As we waited the crew chief, J. J. Harris, spoke to us through the ambulance door.

"Just a few instructions," he said, dead pan. "This flight will be mostly over water. If we have to ditch there are hatches, above, forward, and aft and plenty of life jackets. The plane is noisy and you're supposed to wear ear plugs but this is an emergency and we ain't got any. Nor food, for the same reason. We do have a jug of water but it's not very big. So if we do ditch, and it's plenty hot down there, don't drink unless you're real thirsty."

We looked at each other and prepared to board, all feeling frantically thirsty and reasonably depressed. The pilot, Captain Joe Gervais, snapped us out of it.

"Don't worry," he said. "We've had 15,000 hours together and haven't lost one yet."

The C-130 seemed more like the inside of a tunnel than an airplane. A bed had been rigged for Lois amidships where it was quietest. Sergeant Harris gave her his own ear plugs.

Lois was never more sunny or unaware. "How silly you're going to feel," she said, "when you find there isn't a thing the matter with me." Her pretty hair framed a face vibrant with life, her voice was full, everything about her made me doubt —and how I longed to doubt—the verdict of science.

At 25,000 feet the interior of the plane was achingly cold. Lois was bundled in blankets and seemed not to notice. She felt so well we were even able to get her up periodically, as she loved to watch the clouds. A little headache began to nag, not severe enough to upset her but it made Tom Wilson and me uneasy. We examined her eye grounds again.

The optic disc was filling and there was sign of hemorrhage, evidence of increasing pressure within the skull. The worse her condition grew, the more cheerful Lois became. She asked for her diary so that she could write up her trip. We left her alone with it to give her privacy and to fight down a wish to weep. Thank God the plane was long. I walked off my frustration at knowing what must be done and that there was nothing I could do. I believe I walked to Tokyo.

As the sun set Mary Warner helped Lois up to see the beauty of it, standing by the window holding her hand. The red sky turned purple and faded to dusk and Lois' face lit with delight.

Quite undone I went to my bag, found a bracelet I had bought to bring home to my Helen, and put it round Lois' wrist. She looked at me and blushed with pleasure, stroking it with her other hand. Then she wanted to give me something and fumbled in her purse. All she could find were some peppermint Lifesavers which she insisted Tom and I share since none of us had eaten.

Dear God, I thought, will this plane never land? I had been airborne for close to twenty-four hours and our objective seemed to slip over the horizon endlessly. Perhaps it was an answer that the Seat Belt sign flashed on then when I found waiting almost beyond my endurance. Down we plunged into cold rain where an ambulance waited. Lois quietly insisted that she would walk to it . . . she did feel silly about all the trouble. . . .

It was Saturday night, forty-eight hours since the alarm had been raised. At the hospital Captain William Silvernail, Air Force neurosurgeon, was ready for us. Lois, stoical still, walked to her bed.

On Sunday the sky was lowering. Dr. Bell, Air Force neurologist, and Dr. Silvernail conferred with me in the morning.

It was agreed that an arteriogram be done, an injection of dye which would reveal the condition of the brain and show a tumor if there was one.

Sunday afternoon we knew—a displacement so great that it could be nothing but a tumor, so great that it was probably inoperable.

Lois' condition was worsening and now her body grew rigid and inflexible. The surgeon did not wish to operate until she was more flaccid. For eighteen hours she gradually improved so that on Monday morning Dr. Silvernail was willing to attempt surgery.

When he exposed Lois' brain he saw that the whole left frontal lobe was already destroyed by a growth that was so deep-seated no skill could remove it. He did what he could, knowing it was not enough.

Mercifully, Lois never regained consciousness. But in her death, as in her life, Lois Boyce proclaimed around the world how precious is a single life to all Americans.

Chapter XIX

While I flew on with Lois Boyce, the *Hope* lay in the harbor at Ambon. They say all the navies in the world could anchor there at once. Around its vast perimeter villages dot the hills and rich farms spread out in the sun. Land is plentiful and the Ambonese are proud, intelligent, and industrious. No wonder they resent the Colonial Dutch policy that left them so short of trained men.

Our welcome there was tumultuous. In twenty working days not only did Lally complete his mass X ray and Richard Mark report on the water supply, but our doctors treated 3,500 patients.

How many lives will be affected by our visit? Many! The TB
wards were cleared; the water purified; a blood bank established. Besides this, many Ambonese will see normally again
because Arnold Smoller showed a simple eye operation to a
general practitioner. Ambon's surgeons are so insanely over-
worked they can take only the most urgent cases.

Three children who had never been able to walk took
their first steps on board the *Hope* in that harbor. Little
Hartati, aged three, had been crippled by an illness akin to
polio. The ship's maintenance man made her a posterior splint
and a pair of small crutches. Her mother looked on as she
began to walk. "And," said Sue Glocke, glowing with pride,
"watching the procedure was Miss M. Tomaso from the public
hospital. She has learned the basic principles of physical
therapy from us and she can carry on after we are gone."

The Ambonese would carry on with everything we had
started. They were that kind of people.

What we from the *Hope* remember about Ambon goes far
beyond medicine. Outside of working hours we played tennis
with the Ambonese and danced with them and went with
them on picnics to their powdery white beaches where huge
starfish could be caught in the surf and tiny blue fish flashed
across the coral reefs. When we visited nearby villages they
gathered en masse to cheer us. Johana Vettoretti was asked
to sing over their radio and they sang to us and every
Saturday night they provided special entertainment for us at
the island's only hotel.

The *Hope* had only two more stops scheduled before she
returned to Djakarta, her home base in Indonesia. From there
we would leave Indonesia and head north for Vietnam. Our
human component had full steam up and wanted to accomplish everything possible in the time left to us in the islands.
Our over-age ship was beginning to show signs of exhaustion.

Before we reached Lombok island, the air conditioning
broke down in two operating rooms and two wards. That
meant curtailing work on board, but the staff impatiently
planned to make fuller use of facilities on shore. After all,
Lombok's capital, Mataram, only a short distance from the
port, was an island crossroads and we expected it to be a

modern city. Instead of depending on interisland steamers, Mataram had an airfield where Garuda Convairs were scheduled to arrive twice a week. Instead of being Islamic, Lombok was Hindu—and the Hindus told us this meant they were much more forward-looking. Some of our rotators were leaving us there, but others were due in from Djakarta. Dick Elliott expected a busy time.

It didn't start out like that.

The Garuda planes flew, at least when we were there, confusedly, sometimes refusing to come or to leave and sometimes nesting somewhere else. When they did keep to schedule, little people were bumped by bigger people who were unseated by still bigger ones until only VIP's actually got anywhere. Our rotators whose stint was completed and who were planning to leave from Mataram were lucky. A plane did fly on February 22 and high priorities provided them with seats. Replacements due in from Djakarta weren't so lucky. Their Garuda stranded them on Bali.

As soon as they could they took passage for Lombok on the "African Queen." Surrounded by families, livestock, and the inevitable old bicycle tires on the afterdeck, they watched the mists swirling around the holy mountain of Agung and when they finally reached the port of Ampenan the Hari Raja, a three-day Moslem festival, was in full swing.

They found very little going on. Dick Elliott worried about the insubstantial dock at Ampenan on either side of which export goods were piled on the beach waiting to be picked up. He forbade heavy traffic until the pier was reinforced. In Mataram itself work was unbearbly slow getting under way. Holidays, the tropical tempo, and suspicion combined to keep people away from us. By Friday, just the same, word was around and the pace quickened to what we had come to feel was "normal." Twelve hundred patients applied.

Most of the work was done as it had to be on shore. When the local hospital in Mataram ran out of beds, we concentrated on holding classes. Mantris, with their two years of hospital experience, applied to us for special courses. Fifteen to twenty showed up every morning with a list of what they wanted to learn, including positioning, dressing techniques, and diet therapy. Since there were no classrooms, Dorothy Aeschliman and Ann Roden sat on the edges of ward beds, holding blackboards to illustrate their lectures. Patients in the wards listened, fascinated, smiling and nodding their heads in agreement with everything anyone said. Ten mantris from the Military Clinic joined them for several sessions. After training periods, the mantris practiced what they had learned under their teachers' supervision and with the happy cooperation of the patients.

HOPE surgeons operated on a tight schedule, keeping all the beds full. They had to use gondola operating tables and work under what Mary Damuth described as a spotlight powered by eight fireflies.

Shoes were rare on Lombok and even operating room attendants went barefooted. We tried to convince them that this contributed to cyclic hookworm, but short of providing footwear for the entire population there wasn't much we could do about it. In that warm climate, with the only bath and sanitation facilities public ones, we found that people firmly limited their fluid intake. It wasn't considered socially pleasant to sweat too much or void frequently. This niceness contributed to bladder stones and we did succeed in persuading hospital patients to drink more liquids.

We took only the most pressing cases on the ship. One of these was Sidik, a boy half of whose face was pushed around until it stood at right angles to the other half. He was like a Picasso walking. His type of tumor was not uncommon, but would never have reached such proportions in the U.S. Fortunately he was a healthy young man and could withstand radical surgery. It was amazing that with such distortion the vision in the eye that looked straight into his other eye had not been destroyed. Pulliam gave Sidik a human face, but long-term reconstructive surgery was out of the question. Still, he will live and look like a person and not an artist's wayward reassemblage of features.

Local gratitude for all we did took many forms. One husband whose wife's large thyroid was removed by Dr. Richard Ireton, painted three oil portraits of the three nurses who looked after her and two of the doctor. Nan Campion inspired the most courtly gesture of all. A nine-year-old gallant bowed over her hand when he was discharged and kissed it.

Since Lombok had been a crossroads for rotators, not everybody on the *Hope* had time to get acquainted with everyone else. Nurse Ruth Currie rode back to the ship one afternoon with a pathologist, Dr. Edwin Knights, who had just arrived. As a matter of pride staffers said very little about being homesick, but Ruth was. When she discovered that Knights had been born in Providence, Rhode Island, so near Boston where she had lived for six years, she was delighted to talk with him of home.

Before we sailed on for Semarang, Java (last port before our return to Djakarta where we would leave Indonesia and head north for Vietnam), the two discovered mutual interests that went far beyond nostalgia. They both loved music and they both loved driving through the countryside and visiting Indonesians in each other's company. Claire O'Neil didn't announce the engagement in the Hope newspaper, *Scuttlebutt*, until we were on our way to Saigon, and they weren't married until they both got back to the U.S., but everyone aboard was aware of the *Hope*'s new medical romance.

They were not aware that the ship itself was headed for near-fatal disaster. It was betwen Lombok and Semarang that *Hope* hit bottom.

Indonesian waters are extraordinarily treacherous. Jagged coral reefs protrude from those beautiful volcanic islands. Navigational lights are few and charts are often fifty years old. Even tubs like the *Babut* rarely leave or make port except by daylight, and the *Hope* left or came into harbors only under the sun. Narrow channels were avoided at night. There was one dangerous place between Lombok and Semarang where the course was laid close to the small island of Sapudi. Captain Gerber, who had replaced Captain Windas, left word to be wakened in time to navigate that stretch himself by flashing beacon. He emerged on the bridge to find that he was too late. A ten-foot-high cliff loomed dead ahead. Gerber instantly changed course by 30 degrees and cut speed.

The jolt was so slight that none of the medical staff felt

anything, but chief engineer Strohacker was out of bed in a single leap. Old hands wake up when there's a change in the pitch of the engines and his eyes had popped open the instant the engines slowed.

Florida's Dr. Mark Kuhn wasn't asleep and some uneasy feeling made him pull on his clothes and go out on deck. Shocked to find the ship standing still at 3:30 in the morning, he looked down to see coral through luminous water.

Fortunately the reef on which the *Hope* ran aground was not coral. ("There wouldn't be any bottom left," commented Gerber.) The *Hope's* front end was wedged onto boulders of rock which were sunk in sand and mud beneath shallow water.

As the Hopies woke and joined Kuhn, they found the crew frantically making ready for high tide at nine. "How do you like working on a shore-based hospital again?" Leo Haney asked Ann Crary as he handed her a cup of coffee. "And what say we do a little snorkeling out there?"

The water rose only three feet in the morning tide and driving the engine full speed astern failed to release the ship. There were twelve hours in which to prepare for the next high tide. Overboard went the many thousand-gallon fresh-water supply. Fuel oil was transferred to rear portside tanks to cant the ship. Five-ton anchors were moved by block and tackle with the assistance of launches as far aft as they would go, on a line with the bridge, their flukes aimed to dig into the reef. A rowboat brought out a note from Sapudi asking if we needed help. Captain Gerber said no thanks. Two hundred Hopies, an aggregate fifteen tons, were ordered to the stern before nine.

At full tide, the anchor winches began to turn, engines were ordered full speed in reverse. There was a nerve-racking sound of crunching and scraping. Over the reef the sea was roiled into turbulence as if thrashed by a school of whales. The *Hope* began to move and a great cheer went up.

As she inched backward, one propeller struck a coral pinnacle and the blades were sheered off. It was a grim token of what coral might have done to the hull. In a few minutes the *Hope* was free and Captain Gerber anchored her in deep water, sounded from the launches, for the night. Engineers descended to assess the damage.

Her plates were unbuckled, her second skin undamaged, and she did not ship water. Old though she was, she had come through. The outer skin was ripped as if by a giant oyster knife for over a hundred feet, though, and the gallant vessel listed three degrees. Gerber admitted afterward that he had not believed he could get the *Hope* off that reef and had planned to appeal to Singapore for seagoing tugs to salvage her. That would have cost thousands of dollars and thousands of hours. As it was, every move she made from now on would have to be in the direction of the nearest drydock.

Chapter XX

In Semarang, Java, on the morning of April 29, the Chairman of the Hope committee and the civic and military dignataries representing the city-state waited on the pier that stretches out through shallow water toward the open sea. We were to anchor almost five miles offshore. Hours passed, the temperature rose, noon came. Without lunch, they stood mopping their faces and straining their eyes toward the empty horizon.

Late in the afternoon a car halted with screaming brakes at the end of the long dock and a clerk from the health office dashed out on the pier. His wife, he announced, had just heard on the Voice of America broadcast that the *Hope* would be twenty-four hours late.

Captain Gerber had not been able to rouse Semarang by wireless, but easily got through to San Francisco which got through to Washington. The Voice relayed the message to Indonesia. It had all taken six hours.

The faithful committee came back to greet us when we did get there and opened the heavy schedule which was planned for us with the formalities of introduction.

Our months in the outer islands were over. We were back

on Java and back in civilization. Medical facilities were positively dazzling. A 900-bed public hospital was supplemented by a number of private ones. At the main hospital, a complex of low buildings set in well-tended lawns, Semarang doctors were fluoroscoping and recording the ills of patients waiting for us in a sheltered patio. From a line that stretched around a corner and out of sight, they chose well and they needed us. Their problem was that there were only twenty resident doctors for an area in which 22 million people lived.

Semarang is really two towns. The old one hugs the coast. Its streets are narrow; its godowns or warehouses and houses are densely crowded for protection within a moated wall, now long since crumbled. People here are beasts of burden and old women stoop under mountains of faggots while *betjak* drivers fight a precarious way through snarled traffic and overloaded humans. In the marketplace street vendors sell everything in the world, repair a watch or wash out your eyes for a few rupiahs. The average laboring man makes the equivalent of thrity to fifty cents a day and life for him is wretched and brief.

Inland, modern Semarang spreads over lush hillsides, connected to old Semarang by handsome Bojung Road. Wide avenues converge on the main square where the Dutch Resident once lived. A mosque stands nearby. Through both towns the Semarang River runs between steep, picturesque banks.

We could no longer take cases on the *Hope*. Electricity had become so uncertain that everyone kept a flashlight handy and the air conditioning was now wholly unreliable. Instead we would take advantage of the shore facilities and divide our time between Semarang and Jogjakarta, across the island eighty miles southeast. Both cities were lively and receptive to new ideas.

To bring in the supplies we needed, we became burden carriers ourselves. "We lugged distilled water," said nurse Elizabeth Hammond, "from the launches along that darned dock until we knew every exasperating inch of it." For things too heavy for us, a jeep was occasionally maneuvered precariously out the length of the pier.

Every morning the launch known as the 8:40 Special bore staffers to work in Semarang. Next trip brought the relays bound for a day or two at a time in Jogjakarta. At least we caught up on periodicals, a bit old, but available, in the three-quarter-hour run. From Semarang six teams crossed the highlands during the eighteen days *Hope* was in port—a group leaving the waterfront in a station wagon right after lunch and passing another on its way.

Coming into Jogjakarta, you saw Merapti, a blue-violet cone with a soft plume of smoke hanging in the still air above it. The city itself is surrounded by fertile, well-cultivated fields, the finest in Java. Teak in the forests and opium poppies in the field and edible birds' nests on the cliffsides contribute to prosperity in the countryside. The lovely town itself still shows signs of strafing.

Dilarang masuk berkata Belanda—It is forbidden to speak Dutch. Jogjakarta is called the second Pearl Harbor because the Dutch mounted a sneak attack on it from Semarang airfield on December 19, 1948. Planes bombed and strafed the streets "lengthwise and crosswise," horrifying the civilized world, and then military units captured Sukarno and other "rebels" who later became powerful in the new republic. Within a year the Dutch were gone from Java, but bitterness lingers.

Only after their independence did a native medical cadre begin to develop. There are no old doctors in Jogjakarta, but more young ones are being trained every year. It is possible to predict that the medical profession there will one day be adequate to the need for it, and I believe this will come about sooner than most people dare hope.

Its medical centers are progressive and eager. Marion Wier said, "They asked a lot of us and gave a lot to us." Special knowledge of diseases like malaria, jaundice, and typhoid was shared with us and we were able to leave them with specific and far-from-primitive techniques. Dr. Folger found their electrocardiagraph beyond repair and gave them one of ours plus a course in how to run and mend it. At the eye hospital, Dr. Joan Goble, a rotator who was alternating with her own husband so that they could keep up their practice at home without interruption, transplanted an American cornea, received the week before, to the eye of an Indonesian railroad worker. A local surgeon watched intently. It was the first such procedure demonstrated in the region.

One of our young men, Robert Toth, had already agreed to stay on in Surabaja when his HOPE tour was finished, teaching cytology. The University of California accredited him to their program of medicine in Indonesia for the following year. Now the chief pathologist at Gadja Mahda University in Jogjakarta suggested he use the University as his research center. Toth was delighted. We would leave but he would return.

The University housed us all while we were in Jogjakarta and provided our food. Fortunately this part of Java prefers temperate seasoning and Hopies did not have to pretend to like the food in order not to hurt their hosts' feelings. From University dormitory bedroom windows at night you could see the volcano, Merapti, glowing dull red and occasionally spilling long ribbons of flame. One team woke of a morning to find a fall of ash over the town that was like a London fog. On the ground ashes lay half an inch thick and any movement stirred them into swirling clouds. Ashes packed ears and noses and sifted through clothes. The women wore scarves like mobcaps, but everyone returned to Semarang gray-headed.

In spite of the unremitting rush of work, Sundays were days off and our hosts gave picnics in the all-too-frequent rain. To see the lovely scenery, they took us out in busloads for two and three hours at a time. "Indonesian buses must be built by elves for elves," wrote Ann Crary. "They are also specially designed to channel rain down your neck and into your lap. Your lap is forced into a receptive cup by lack of leg room. You get out looking and feeling as if you had spent several hours in a defective spin dryer."

As it was everywhere, our last act was to leave supplies for the medical center and thousands of pounds of milk. "Exchange was excellent. Entire operation in Semarang," reported Marion Wier succinctly, "conclusive proof of workability and value of our basic belief in better understanding of peoples."

The *Hope* returned to Djakarta 211 days, two hours, and twenty minutes after leaving it. We were welcomed like a victorious army (and were just about as battered). They knew what had been accomplished and they thanked us with a staggering program of entertainment. Even though we went on working, the Indonesians feted us as if this were our holiday.

It was a time of good-byes. Four buses and three jeeps trekked up a twisting highway into the mountains to the 400-year-old town of Bandung. The first-year class of the Bandung Nursing School which had sailed with us 212 days earlier was coming home. We were going there for our last mission in Indonesia.

Since the middle of the nineteenth century Bandung had been used as a hill station by the Dutch and other Europeans who could not tolerate the lowlands during the hot season. It is a cool, sparkling town, high above sea level, circled by tea and cinchona plantations. Recently it had become the center for manufacturing pharmaceutical supplies and for a pilot medical project with training schools and laboratories. It is the dream of Indonesia to give all their towns equal facilities.

We held classes and seminars in the Department of Health auditorium. Discussion was open, honest, and exciting. The doctors were the cream of the crop in Indonesia and the hospitals had high standards and, so rare in the Orient, well-kept records. We spread out to lecture. Betty Ahern and Joanne Hefelfinger went to the Bandung Mother and Child Service Nurses and Hazel Wessel to the School of Nutrition at Bogor. Before we left, we wanted to leave as much teaching as possible behind us.

The local HOPE committee arranged a trip to the nearest volcano for the first team, and halfway up the bus's brakes gave out and they were transferred to an assortment of vehicels, including a police jeep complete with flashing red light and blaring siren. The way twisted through woods where fir trees grew beside palm ferns and past steep hillsides terraced into paddies.

Tangkuban Prahu has three craters. Several Americans, among them Stan Abrams and Jim Yates, climbed down inside one where lava bubbled and smoke rose. Earlier travelers had taken rocks and spelled out USSR. In short order these were rearranged and the rocks spelled SS HOPE USA.

Nurses from Bandung who had been with us all this time said good-by tearfully. Zahara Daulay, a great favorite, said, "The first time I put my feet on the *Hope* it looked like a strange world. I was between people who were tall and a different color from me. Because we were all nurses I forgot the differences when we started to work. I began to feel at home in a few hours, but when I started in the operating room I felt uncertain again. But I had a patient teacher who knew her job. It was all right. And then I found out that she loved tennis and music and the gap between races stopped being there."

On May 22 the first Bandung team came back to relieve the skeleton staff on the *Hope* who took their places in Bandung. Four days later all the *Hope*'s American staff was united in Djakarta for the last of the official parties. These wound up with a reception on the spacious lawn of the Ministry of Health where a model of the *Hope* had been sculptured in flowers. General Satrio made a heart-warming speech of farewewll and presented us with a tray handmade of Jogjakarta silver on which was engraved: "The people of Indonesia acclaim the meritorious service of the SS *Hope* and express pride in the exemplary co-operation between the American and Indonesian participants during *Hope*'s stay in Indonesia from October 19, 1960 to June 1, 1961."

At nine o'clock on June's first morning, the ship moved away from the pier at Tandjung Priok while Indonesian hands held the ends of colored streamers which ran up to American hands on board. Gifts had been exchanged by fast friends; embraces and tears had marked many partings. Across the water, as the ribbons snapped one after another, messages were called back and forth. One little nurse, half laughing, half crying, shouted, "Don't forget *napas dalam, batuk* and *minum banjak*—Breathe deeply, cough and drink." When indi-

vidual voices could no longer be heard, the Indonesian nurses
on the pier formed a circle and sang the Indonesian ballads
our people loved to hear.

The *Hope* set her course for Hong Kong to be drydocked
and repaired before she sailed on for another far country, for
Vietnam. During seven days the weary staff could rest, as if
they were passengers on a luxury liner, or a kind of luxury
liner. A massive sigh went up all over the ship. In it was the
sound of regret for leaving, satisfaction at what we had left
behind, and pure bone weariness.

In seven and a half months we had treated more than
17,000 people, performed more than 700 major operations,
held more than 800 teaching sessions, X-rayed 10,000, distributed 86,000 pounds of medical equipment, 80,000 pounds
of powdered milk, 4,000 medical journals and the same number
of books, and 2,000 artificial limbs. And 30,000 visitors had
seen our ship.

We had done yeoman service. Teachers we had been, and
our students made us proud. Students we had been and were
taking on with us what we had learned. The outpouring
from the American cornucopia was staggering. And it was
reaching the people who needed it, directly, simply, never
lost at a top level. Also we had sat on beaches, eaten peanuts,
and talked to people. Personal. Human. People to other
people.

Part IV

Hope in Vietnam

Chapter XXI

The HOPE is a great idea. It is an ideal working. I can state this now where I could only believe in it and argue for it before 1961. It isn't I nor the board of directors nor the staffs of doctors nor even the core of gallant women nor the vessel with her twice-ripped hull and patched-up machinery. It is the idea and the ideal that has come through. Every man, woman, and child who so much as put a nickel in the HOPE milk cartons may take credit and have confidence. I say this in humility with pride. We have gone on, will go on. Because in Indonesia we learned about ourselves and in Vietnam we proved the worth of what we had learned.

Vietnam was in a state of war. The *Hope* was shot at in the Saigon River by Communist guerrillas. There was civil strife in the capital city of Saigon where we docked. Buddhists and Christians and various political forces were in conflict under the "interim" government of Ngo Dinh Diem. Refugees from the North, from the so-called Vietcong under Ho-Chi-Minh, did not mingle well with the South Vietnamese, and that created another source of conflict. French influence was still very strong and the French had not forgiven Americans for failing to come to their rescue at Dienbienphu where they lost French Indo-China.

Furthermore we of the *Hope* had inter-American problems to contend with. The U.S. government was deeply involved in Vietnam and had its own medical program, the USOM. Instead of welcoming us, a few of their officers were resentful and obstructive.

I realized the odds against us when I met Dr. Willard Boynton, chief medical officer of the American Medical Mission in Vietnam, and a committee of Vietnamese doctors in February. Our Washington anti-HOPE clique had advised Dr. Boynton "officially" that we might not even get to Saigon. We were indeed having financial problems as we had not been able to capitalize yet on our achievements in Indonesia. Rather than be identified with a disappointment or a farce, the Vietnamese were considering a withdrawal of their invitation to us.

We had asked Dr. Boynton and Dr. An, Vietnamese representative on our Saigon HOPE committee, to visit us in Indonesia, suggesting various times when we would be working on board, tied up at a dock as we would be in Saigon. Unfortunately they appeared in Semarang, which couldn't have been more misleading. The ship was anchored miles offshore and the staff scattered over the city and as far off as Jogjakarta. The two doctors reported back to Saigon that HOPE had only "six doctors" on board. With Boynton and An was Miss Tersa Morgan, chief nurse for USOM and an old Cochin-China hand. She controlled the training for nurses under American aegis in Saigon and it was she who would select the student nurses to study on the *Hope*. If she did not cooperate, we were in for trouble. Not only nurses but labor, cooks, aides, and other students would avoid us. Her power was great and perhaps she did not relish the notion of another chief nurse in a place where this position is so honored.

The State Department in Washington came through with authorization for us to proceed to Saigon and complete our mission as planned. Our impact had been so strong in Indonesia the department thought it vital to American interests that we continue in Vietnam. Now that that was settled, we had to create a climate for our work in Saigon and to stop fighting other Americans. (Serving the same ends, why do we waste our substance in fractricidal disagreements?)

To get things ready, to dissipate both antipathy to us and rosy, unrealizable visions, I sent an advance team to Saigon. Craig Leman went from the *Hope* and was quickly joined by Martie Kohn, Philip Fleuchaus, Joan Goble, and Rufus and Dorothy Morrow. I met them there early in June to find that Dr. Kohn had gradually taken charge. We never could decide whether Martie was so popular with the Vietnamese because of his ability or inability to speak French. As Martie said, "I may not speak it well, but I speak it loud. And the louder I speak, the more they seem to understand."

One all-important person began to understand, thanks to Martie. Dr. Fan Hu Chuong was president of the syndicate of private doctors. A refugee from Hanoi in the North, a profound Buddhist and an enemy of Diem's regime, he had been in jail for opposing Diem, but he was a very powerful figure in Saigon just the same. If he said so, the syndicate of French-trained local medical men would support us rather than oppose us.

Martie is six-foot-two, Jewish, aggressive, competent, and stubborn. Fan Hu Chuong is a martinet, energetic, quick-moving, capable, violently nationalistic, and about five feet tall. They confronted each other like boxers, bantam and heavy. Martie bent over the man who came up roughly to his belt buckle and shouted at him in French only to find that Dr. Chuong, small as he was, could shout louder and gesticulate more vigorously. Furthermore he preferred to speak in Vietnamese at machine-gun speed and refused to be interrupted for interpretation until he had finished whatever he wanted to say. After several furious encounters, the two men became respectful friends and Chuong's help was invaluable.

There was considerable rivalry between the private practitioners and the government doctors. Dr. An, who worked for the Department of Health directly under the Minister of Health, Dr. De, was not fond of Chuong. He spoke of him as a Northerner who did not really understand the South and who thought Southerners were lazy. Dr. An himself was the antithesis of Chuong in appearance and character—round of face, constantly laughing, and very friendly. He did his best for us, as a committee member, but he stood very much in awe of his boss, Dr. De.

Dr. De, on his part, was standoffish and ceremonious, like many Asian bureaucrats. Besides his duties as Health Minister, he maintained a gorgeous private clinic, five stories high, where each wealthy patient had a grand suite of his own. There's nothing comparable to De's hotel-hospital in the U.S. On top of it in an outdoor penthouse, he entertained hundreds of people with his beautiful wife as hostess. A highly sophisticated man and an excellent obstetrician, he had taken part of his training in the U.S., spoke excellent English, was a stickler for protocol, and disliked Dr. Chuong. No matter how we handled things somebody's feelings always got ruffled.

When I got there, I found that the advance contingent had made extraordinary progress all the same. Half the prominent citizens of Saigon had asked Martie to examine them and local doctors, who complained about this, were also demanding his attention. "Well, Bill," Martie explained blandly, "what am I going to do? They say I'm the finest diagnostician in all the U.S."

"You're good," I admitted, "but where did they get that impression?"

Martie looked at me owlishly through black-rimmed glasses and shrugged. "Simple. I told them."

Actually his reputation was fine for us. With the others from Hope, he had managed to visit each of ten hospitals in the area and 11,000 patients had applied to Hope. This figure was bound to grow to at least 40,000 and we asked the Vietnamese committee to process the applicants.

There was a certain amount of hanky-panky going on that we wanted to clean up. Some few doctors were collecting fees for referring patients to Hope. Poor devils gave hoarded savings to these corrupt men in return for a promise of free treatment from us. These same doctors promised their rich patients attention by the Americans as a matter of prestige. If we could weed out such practices and process out routine cases, impossible ones, and prestige patients, we could do a very great deal of good.

Rallying to our aid, three Vietnamese doctors did us brilliant service. Buck-toothed Dr. Dan, director of the city receiving hospital, was anxious to help, anxious to learn, and a steadying influence whenever we ran into factionalism. He worked with Kohn and Smoller at the screening clinic.

Dr. Hao, professor of medicine, first-class internist, and a director of the school of nursing, was likewise dedicated. He and Martie became close friends. A small man, from the North like Dr. Chuong, he was sweet, cultured, and never raised his voice as he puffed away at cigarettes in a delicate ivory holder.

Later on Martie arranged for Hao to come to the U.S. as his guest and to study American methods. Alas, no exit visa has been forthcoming from his government. Vietnam is afraid of losing the skills of such men. A good many doctors from the North have funds in the U.S. and want to travel. Able men like Hao would be welcome anywhere. Most of them stay on in Saigon, of necessity or not. They are brave to stay. If the South does fall to the North, they are marked men, looked upon as community leaders and dangerous.

Dr. Tam, dean of the medical school, also cooperated after a period of initial coolness, sending students to train with us. This was in spite of resentment on the part of the French members of his faculty. They felt that ours was an intrusion in territory where their influence was still strong.

We never did get along with the French. It was too bad, but they felt that our coming was a slap at them and we may have been too open in finding their teaching methods outdated. Also perhaps it was a diplomatic error not to consult with them sooner and more closely. But we had to deal directly with the Vietnamese who, on their side, were trying to take over from the French.

If it hadn't been for one American we would have trod on more toes than we did. William Piaff, USIS man in Saigon, was married to a Vietnamese girl, spoke her language as well as French, and was committed to HOPE from the start. With the exception of the American Ambassador, Fred Nolting, Piaff did us more good than any other local American. He obtained excellent press coverage for us, the kind that presented our case without arousing false dreams. Piaff never forgot that his job was to forward American interests in the country where he was stationed. The *Hope*, he thought, was a visible and marvelous way to show America at its best.

Literally taking me by the hand, he led me through the intricacies of dealing with the Vietnamese. Together we visited a roster of municipal officials.

One possible source of trouble, for instance, was that the crew of the *Hope* might go a bit wild in Saigon after so many months in the back country. There were plenty of temptations just off the dock. We did not want the Communists to make propaganda out of the natural behavior of American seamen. I told the Mayor that we asked no special courtesy or immunity because we were from the *Hope*. What we desired was peace. If any of our men misbehaved, put them in jail, keep them there, and notify us. Much relieved, His Honor the Mayor set aside an area of his favorite jail for the few troublemakers and overbibulous enthusiasts among our 130 merchant mariners and took prompt care of them.

We kept our basic plans for the medical program broad and flexible. To take the initiative away from twenty-five to thirty of the finest physicians from the U.S. would be absurd. In outline, each doctor would consult with two Vietnamese doctors in his specialty and work out his own program. It still astounds me how well they did this and how easily each man's program fitted into an organized, effective, orderly operation.

On the morning of June 15 we were as ready as we could manage. Martie, Mr. Powell of the American Embassy, and I set out for Cap St. Jacques to meet the *Hope*. Cap St. Jacques, where the Annamese cordillera and the Saigon River reach the sea, is no great distance from the capital and we would have liked to drive down, but Saigon was an uneasy oasis ringed by hostility. The roads ran through no-man's land. The town of Cap St. Jacques, once a favorite summer resort for the Saigonese, was cut off and out of bounds.

We flew directly to the small airport and were hustled by car to the boathouse. On the way we passed what had once been an agreeable vacation hotel. Pockmarked with shots and dilapidated now, we were told it still got some custom from soldiers training nearby.

The rich delta, with its succession of paddies which produced enough rice to export a million pounds a year, looked forlorn. Food and the potential revenue were badly needed, but to transport the crops to Saigon, sole port along the seacoast, was dangerous. Roads were barred and the Vietcong held stretches of river bank and attacked tugs and junks moving upstream.

At the boathouse a French pilot waited to bring the *Hope* thirty-four miles upriver to Saigon. We clambered aboard his tug with him as the ship came over the horizon, majestic,

glistening in her fresh coat of paint, riding on a brand-new
bottom and heading toward the channel at a fine clip.

The sea was calm and we were impatient with the pilot
who took his time about getting under way. When we were
about a mile and a half to port, the *Hope* tooted a greeting,
but instead of veering close to us, Captain Gerber continued
merrily on his course. M. le Pilote threw up his hands and
began to jabber furiously.

"*Il est fou, le maître,* crrrazy. *Mon dieu, mon dieu.* There
is a sonken sheep somewhere there. Your capitaine cannot
know. . . . *Il marche trop vite.* Too fast! If he hits . . ." The
Frenchman made a graphic gesture of a ship nosing down-
ward. "In ten minutes, all will be over. Wave!" he besought
us. "*Signalez!*"

We flailed our arms and shouted until our throats ached.
The pilot screamed instructions in French and made sweeping
motions as if to draw the ship toward us. I snatched up binoculars to see if our frantic messages were understood.

Hopies lined the rail. Everyone looked fresh and happy,
rested from five days at sea and a six-day vacation in Hong
Kong. Hong Kong's cheap and whirlwind tailors had made
dazzling improvements in frayed wardrobes. The girls had
their hair fresh done and still wore flowers bought two days
ago in the Hong Kong market. I can't tell you how splendid
and charming they looked—and how relaxed.

After all we had gone through to get this ship to Saigon,
was she going to sink in the mouth of the river while I stood
powerless to avert disaster?

Martie was white. He turned to me when he realized that
our semaphoring was useless and said, "For God's sake, Bill,
you're always bragging about the guardian angel that watches
over HOPE. Pray, damn it, pray."

We three Americans folded our arms on our chests, the
way children do when they recite their Now-I-lay-me's, closed
our eyes, and asked God please for a miracle.

The pilot yelled, "*Mon dieu, c'est un miracle!*" We opened
our eyes. The ship had passed right over the wreck.

Pounding each other on the back, we bellowed with relief.
God did love the *Hope*. HOPE's angel was on the job.

Gerber brought the ship to a halt and we came up to her.

There was oil slick on the surface of the sea. Our old girl had ridden across the submerged obstacle on a cresting wave, abetted by her unseemly speed, but had torn a gash in her fine new bottom over 200 feet long. Her two skins were as good as three lives, but she was in bad shape. At least one tank was holed. As we climbed the gangplank, we were greeted with warmth and merriment. No one had the slightest idea how close the *Hope* had been to shipwreck.

The top deck was cleared for our trip up the river. Patrol boats came out now to meet us and run interference between the *Hope* and the enemies on shore who might snipe at her or lob rifle grenades in her direction. Two Vietnamese helicopters flew overhead, too. As we called the staff together for a briefing session in the classroom, the ship began to list and the floor tipped irritatingly. The day was hot and on either side of the river jungle overspread marshy earth. When we glanced out of portholes we saw few signs of life and none of greeting. The mood of the *Hope* turned somber.

Powell finished his official briefing with a series of warnings. Saigon looked peaceful and prosperous and the people were amiable, but the city was honeycombed with Vietcong agents and with Vietnamese counteragents and with double agents who beclouded every issue. It was inadvisable to talk too freely or to walk out at night.

After the triumph against odds and the grueling work in Indonesia and the brief spree in Hong Kong, the staff of the *Hope* had come to Vietnam in the highest spirits. It was sad to see these plummet.

Chapter XXII

When we rounded the last bend in the river and were allowed back on deck, the Hopies lined the rails again. If they looked less relaxed and cheerful, they had rallied as they always did and were able to smile.

On the marshy river shores no people had gathered to

wave us in. Outside of strongly held centers the population
was fearful of displaying any pro-American sentiment. Retri-
bution could be swift and terrible. As we moved into the large
harbor basin, we saw the first signs of welcome. The dock
had been extended 200 feet to accommodate *Hope's* 530-foot
length and along the old dock a crowd waited for us. Through
glasses I could see Ralph Bellamy, the stage and film star
whom NBC had sent as narrator for a television show about
us. Standing easily, hands on hips, with the actor's assurance
of focusing attention, he wore an open-necked shirt and
white slacks. I could not spot Dr. Chuong yet, but saw some
nurses in uniform and assumed that they were our Vietnamese
students. That meant to me that we would also have cooks,
attendants, and laborers to help us and could move swiftly
into service as a hospital.

The maneuver to the dock required superb seamanship.
The ship had to be turned completely around and brought
alongside stern first. It seemed to take forever. Finally just
as she was edged into position, the rapid current—about nine
knots in this river—caught her broadside and she swung against
the dock, splintering nearly seventy feet of its brand-new
extension, built for us by our friends. As if that wasn't enough,
when we steadied alongside and were ready to disembark,
we found that the Captain and the American President Line
had misunderstood each other. There was no gangway provided for us. It was an inauspicious debut.

Our sea gangway did not reach the pier. The foot of it
ended about level with the shoulders of Dr. Chuong, who
was scheduled to come aboard and lead the welcoming ceremonies. Revising plans in a hurry, we rushed down to meet
him instead while the boatswain hunted for boxes to put under
the suspended gangway. Boxes in place, we half lifted, half
pushed the tiny doctor up and over and along to see the ship
for which he had waited so many months.

When we all disembarked, the warmth of the greetings,
the presentation of traditional bouquets, and the sight of all
those people made us feel optimistic again. Not for long.
During conferences which began at once we discovered that
agreements our advance team considered firm were nothing of

the kind. Nurses had not been assigned to us by Tersa Morgan. The thirty-seven cooks, laborers, and attendants weren't coming. For two days we stewed and struggled, insisting that we concentrate on a teaching program before we attempt to function as a hospital. Ralph Bellamy and the NBC crew idled while they waited for something to film.

Then Dick Elliott decided to close down two wards on the *Hope* until Vietnamese help was forthcoming. As soon as we took this unequivocal position, everything fell into place and enough assistance did show up.

Medical students on vacation besieged us, giving up their free time to be with the *Hope*. We had all the applicants we could accommodate and just as soon as we got in direct contact with the Vietnamese young people it was thrilling. Never had we met students thirstier for knowledge, more open to us. Initial hostility was easy to dispel. They had grown up under the domination of European powers and their curiosity about America was insatiable. Critical they were, but the astonishing thing was to discover how adverse propaganda had backfired. If we were so much attacked, they reasoned, we must have something to attack. Our enemies must fear us to shout epithets so loudly. Many of these educated Vietnamese could speak English and all of them spoke French. Our library was put to constant use. They read and read and read.

Nurses began to come aboard, too, in spite of delays and confusion. They wore native gowns, very pretty ones, traditionally patterned, which we assumed to be made of Oriental silk. Alas for progress and the interruption of Chinese imports, the dresses were rayon. No fabric creates static electricity more readily. Mavis Pate had to get them into cottons before permitting any nurses in the operating rooms. The ladies refused to expose so much as their ankles. Hospital dresses worn over surgeons' scrub pants solved the problem. The small Saigon girls were modestly if unaesthetically engulfed.

Relationships ripened with tropical swiftness. Young medics who took nothing on our say-so did not remain aloof as they worked shoulder-to-shoulder with our doctors. The Americans treated them with a grave politeness, deeply appreciated by the Orientals. As for the women, after a short, decisive battle over the question of three-hour postprandial siestas, the trainee-nurses accepted our strenuous American schedule and the Americans found them pretty and sympathetic and bright.

Even the impediment of language served the cause of friendship. Vietnamese, like Chinese, to which it is related, is a language of tones. Where Indonesian was possible for us to learn, Vietnamese was not. Unless one considered that Martie spoke French, few of us could claim much more than a rusty high-school acquaintance with it. We all used pantomime, stammering attempts to find *parlez-vous-français* phrases, and gesticulation for direct communication. It was the laughter we shared over these efforts that bridged our differences.

A good-natured rivalry sprang up between HOPE veterans and rotators who had not been with us in Indonesia. The newly arrived were horrified by tales of primitive conditions on the islands and the veterans pointed out that we had been freer in the jungle than we were here, docked at the foot of a great shopping street in a metropolis. We were warned again not to walk out at night and no one was supposed to leave the city limits without guards, guides, and special arrangements.

Nor could anyone come on board without passing through a military cordon thrown around us for our protection. The dock was fenced off by troops. Soldiers patroled the harbor in speedboats. All packages were opened for inspection. To keep a Vietcong patriot disguised as a visitor from blowing himself up in order to take us with him, no one was allowed to carry bundles aboard until they were opened and inspected. So that patients would not smuggle in explosives, they were all dressed in HOPE pajamas at shore screening clinics and brought to the gangway in our own buses. After dark, arc lights illumined the vessel and the water around it to prevent marauders from sneaking up on us. We were protected from our invisible enemies and thus cut off to some extent from our friends. The area outside the cordon was always full of people who simply stood and stared at the *Hope*, sometimes staying half the night.

On board, the *Hope* was again a hospital, operating at an intensive level of concentration in devitalizing heat. It seemed like one thing too many to permit a film about us to be made while we worked under such pressure in such conditions.

Ralph Bellamy and director Fred Rheinstein made this remarkably painless. Fred worked at such a fever pitch that we had to treat his ulcer. As for Ralph, he became one of the best friends HOPE ever made. At first he was dispassionate. He knew nothing of the East and of us only that he had a job to do for NBC narrating our story. In the beginning he worried about his clothes and hair and camera angles and lighting. After forty-eight hours he would have been photographed cheerfully in dirty dungarees and nothing to do with the film was allowed to interfere with the hospital. He was a committed Hopie and he made ward rounds, helped with patients, learned all the whys and wherefores of routine, took part in wardroom discussions and Happy Hour chatter. In the nurses he loved and admired like Nancy Campion he found a dedication he had forgotten existed. New friends like Martie Kohn, Craig Leman, and Priscilla Strong introduced him to a world as far as could be from Hollywood. A compassionate man, his eyes saw the misery of the East and his heart understood what we were trying to accomplish. If he could have, he would have stayed with us all three months.

The film when it was done reflected his understanding and devotion. Fred Rheinstein had received permission to accompany one of our teams into Vietcong country. Ralph went along and that material was full of derring-do, an eastern western. But his heart was with the ship where he centered the story on a single waif. Ta van Tu was a dejected tyke suffering from escopia, which meant that he had no depth perception and his eyes focused together only briefly. On his right hand he had a second thumb. He wasn't going to die. Like Mala, without medical help he would have lived on—deformed and useless. Ralph loved the child. When Tu went into the operating room, Ralph held his right hand.

Tu came out of the bandages to take a cheeky place in the world around him. He had a big friend who spoiled him and big plans for a great big future and he looked marvelous.

As Ralph had seen, one child is all children and one helping hand given to a small sufferer all helping hands. President Ngo Dinh Diem visited the *Hope* one day and young Tu, with no idea who he was, spoke up happily and offered to tell him about his operation. Ralph told Tu Diem's identity and the boy hid his face in his hands and laughed at himself. The documentary, when it was shown in the U.S. that September, effectively combined the drama of a field trip into enemy territory with the story of a Saigon boy made whole. Nor did Ralph's services to us end there—he will still drop anything and go anywhere to tell the story of HOPE and of Tu.

Work on board in Saigon was overmatched by work in the city on shore. "A ten-piastre ride from the ship," Sue Glocke wrote to friends at Beekman-Downtown Hospital in New York, "finds us at the Saigon Bien Vien Hospital where daily, Monday through Friday, we hold clinics between half-past two and half-past five. They are not the bedlam of milling crowds, smiling faces, and laughing children we had to push through in Indonesia. Here the patients, one parent to each child, line up quietly on brown benches strung along the walls. Each one is silent, serious, and pathetic and each one has a card, pink, green, yellow, or blue, to indicate which clinic to wait at, with a number that tells the order of their turn to be seen.

"As the clinic begins the patients start moving into the examining rooms. Heartbreak House is open for business."

By taxi, another seven and a half piastres' worth, Sue arrived at the Children's Bellevue Hospital, government-operated and free. Most hospitals were like those in Indonesia, one story high and laid out in a series of connecting rectangles, but this one was only five years old and different. The head nurse, Miss Hoa, boasted that Saigon had begun to build up rather than out. Bellevue was four stories high.

In the admitting clinic three residents and a sixth-year medical student saw an average of 600 youngsters a day. If a child was diagnosed as sufficiently ill to receive treatment, the mother usually went with him into the hospital and stayed the whole time. Small patients were fed, but not parents. Each mother was given a plate, a metal cup and spoon, and she fetched rice cakes wrapped in banana leaves for herself from a corner vendor.

Priorities were tight for the 300 beds, and if a doctor scheduled an operation for a child, chances were he couldn't perform it or opt a bed for a week. Mothers and children waited on the second floor in a big room where the women squatted in corners and along the walls holding the young ones in their arms or with their sick heads in their laps.

"When a crib is vacant," wrote Sue, "the child is assigned to his place in the wards. Mothers have to be forcibly discouraged from creeping into cribs with their children. Many manage to do so anyway.

"Isolation begins and ends with putting contagious diseases in separate wards. It's not much use. Mothers run from ward to ward all over the hospital visiting their cronies.

"At the end of the third-floor hall we saw a diet kitchen where the cook keeps a pot of carrots in their jackets boiling all day long. These he mashes in their juice, combined with water from boiled rice, and serves to youngsters with diarrhea. It is said to be a *sure cure!*"

Only orphans were permitted to double or triple in a single bed, lying vertically, and tended by women from the orphanages.

Ten more piastres would take you as far as Cho Ray Hospital. The wards there were miserably small and nursing techniques shocked even our case-hardened jungle-frontier veterans. On iron cots straw mattresses were covered with a single sheet and the inevitable Dutch pillow. Washstands stood between the rows. Orthopedic patients came and went on a system which permitted them to take a dozen treatments, go home for several weeks, and return for a second series. If there was no marked improvement, the patient was discharged as hopeless.

In Indonesia we had found that with a large family, a mother will demand *obat* for the child who has cerebral palsy or polio, but has no time to give the little one daily exercise. In Vietnam it was the reverse. A mother devoted all her time to the one sick child and let the others run wild.

The cases we could take on board were funneled through

On the fence, nurses; in the middle distance, actor Ralph Bellamy
and director Fred Rheinstein; on the horizon, *Hope*

Flowers and welcome to Saigon for head nurse Claire O'Neil, Vietnamese nurse, and Dr. Walsh
(*USIA-USOM photo*)

In Saigon *Hope* tied up to the riverfront esplanade, which did not prevent the Vietcong from taking pot shots at her on July 4

Johana Vettoretti, chief medical secretary, kept the record straight
and shared her knowledge with Chirana Djohor   (*USIS photo*)

Tu

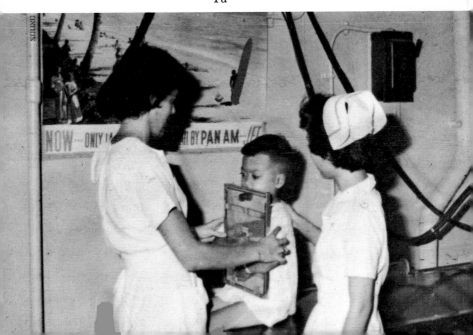

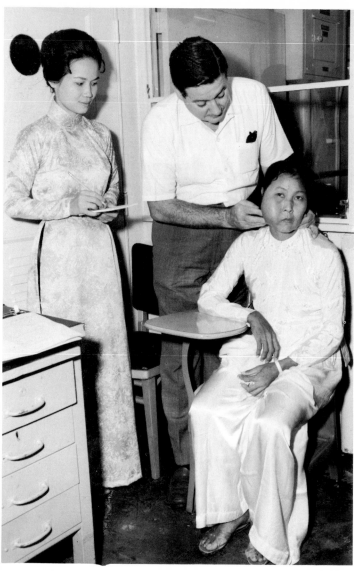

Rich and poor were admitted for treatment—the only criterion was need for help. Dr. Walsh examines a well-dressed and very ill Saigonese

Spilled out onto mats, these babies are in a nursery for lepers

Blindness was everywhere, caused by many conditions and diseases.
Men like Dr. Tisher fought it tirelessly

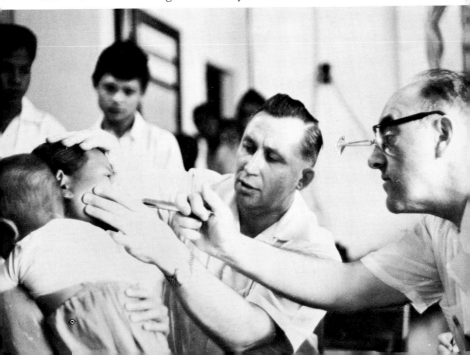

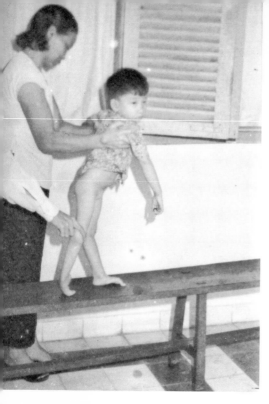

Under HOPE direction and with his mother's cooperation, miraculously this stork-like boy grew straight and learned to walk

Dr. Martie Kohn and Dr. Gogien Koo, who carried on after our departure, examine a hospitalized man

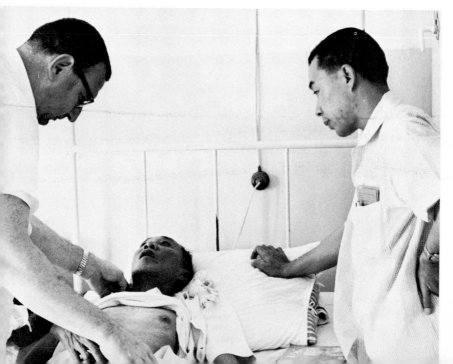

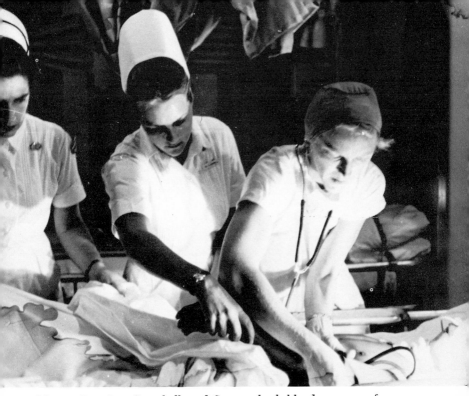

Nurses Campion, Campbell, and Strong check blood pressure of a critically ill patient in the intensive care unit

Dr. Walsh presents the Health Service of Vietnam with invaluable supplies, symbolically represented by HOPE milk cartons

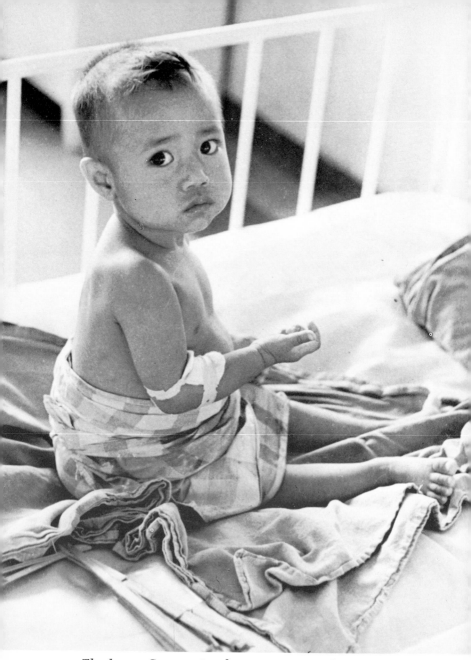

Thank you. Come again—please come again. Thousands of voices, young and old, seemed to echo across the Pacific as we sailed for home

the Central Hospital and carried from there by bus through the peaceful-seeming luxurious heart of the city. Laid out in the manner of the French Second Empire, Saigon has very wide, tree-bordered avenues lined with colorful shops where they sell everything in the world. Elegant women stroll by in exquisite costumes, brilliant-hued long tunics slit up the sides to reveal trousers in white or black. Their sandals have odd round heels and their wide hats protect them from the down-pouring sun and the quick, sporadic rains. Between blazing white walls on the wide streets, water buffaloes contend with Renault taxis and well-dressed pedestrians, reminding you that beyond the marshes across the harbor the country is very primitive. Police and soldiers are everywhere, ringing the public buildings, making you realize, even in the peaceful streets, that a state of war exists.

Signs of war were dramatic in the military hospital. When plastic surgeon John Williams went there on July 17 he found fourteen injured brought in the night before from a skirmish in the vicinity. "Horrible burns, with loss of hands, eyes, and everything from incendiary burns," he reported. "Twelve Vietnam soldiers, they say, were killed and they estimated about a hundred Commies lost. Today we could hear artillery fire from the dock, but it was probably miles away. Saigon on the surface is a very peaceful city."

In the Chinese section, on Saigon's outskirts, poverty was disastrously evident. Marsh-settlements of houses on stilts were so crowded that twenty slept in one small room. People bathed and functioned in the same water and if a match were dropped anywhere a thousand homes would go up in flames. Undernourished as they were, the children had the sweet look of Malaysians and, chirping like sparrows, picked up what crumbs they could to scrape through from day to day. Every few feet along the streets, youngsters sold things, from chewing gum to razor blades or shoelaces or offered to shine your shoes for a piastre or two.

Beyond the center of the city you saw everywhere the tragic overflow of war. Hundreds of thousands of refugees had poured in from the North, swelling the population of Saigon suddenly to over three million. Even once immensely prosperous Hanoi merchants lived in the streets, eating food sickening to see in a world of clamorous filth. There was no room for them and only reluctant welcome. Natives of Saigon looked on the Northerners as carpetbaggers, taking a share of the wealth which the South could ill afford, leaving less for the Southerners. Men from the North, often more sophisticated and better trained, considered themselves more capable and found the Southerners feckless and lazy. It was not an easy situation. It never is. The invaders are homesick and the hosts wish they would and could go home.

When we asked patients from the North, riddled with disease, why they had come, why they had not stayed at home where it couldn't be worse for them than it was here, they often answered, "We prefer freedom."

In the North the battle for freedom had been lost, but while it went on in the South, we could do no less than what we could. To help as much as possible, we sent teams from HOPE both toward the North and farther South into the delta. Ralph Bellamy and I went along on the expedition to Can Tho in the South.

Chapter XXIII

The sun rose with indecorous haste. In the Orient it is not there and then there in a single instant.

On deck eleven of us moved quietly and spoke only when we needed to in husky early-morning voices as we threaded between cartons and bundles. Four, including me, were doctors, three men, one woman—two internists, a surgeon, a pediatrician. There were also a nurse, a nurse-anesthetist, a pharmacist, a journalist, a movie director, an actor, a cameraman.

Beyond the ship, in the muddy water of the Saigon River, a launch continued the patrol that went on ceaselessly for our safety, day and night. Below, on the dock, an armed guard stood at the gate, gun to shoulder.

No one gave a signal but as if there had been a word of command, each of us picked up a flight bag and a box or bundle and started down the long gangway. In the fenced riverside area Dr. An was waiting by a Volkswagen bus in which we hastily stowed our gear. As we drove through the gate the guard saluted. It was 5:30.

The city of Saigon was beginning to stir awake, the dock-front esplanade smelling of dampness from the night's invariable rain. Along Tu Do Avenue, shutters were up on shop-fronts, and two blocks from the waterfront, at a Chinese tailor's, there was an iron grill over wooden doors. The car stopped and the movie director got out and pounded on them, shattering the quiet. A moment later the proprietor pulled open the doors, shoved back the grill, and gave him a bush shirt, refitted overnight for the actor.

We swung down the avenue between solid, masonry build-ings, shaded with trees, and headed for the airport, riding in silence, a little tense, remote from each other yet linked in anticipation of the trip ahead.

At the airport there was no military plane. A World War II DC-3 should have been ready. Dr. An and the chauffeur exploded from the car, embarrassment plain on their faces, and went into the operations shack to confer. They were soon back. Wrong airport. This was civilian; where we belonged was military, fortunately close by.

Our Dakota was waiting, engines turning over, door open. We piled in our impedimenta, then hiked ourselves over the high sill and settled down in the bucket seats.

The door was slammed, the propellers turned, and the plane swung up over Saigon in a long, banking turn. Reaching her plodding top speed of 160 miles an hour, she set a southeast course over green, hilly country, interspersed with flooded rice fields, and in a short time picked up the Mekong River.

I looked around. We were, except for our actor who looked undeniably handsome, not a dressy lot. The medical con-tingent had on white shirts and any old sort of work pants. Dr. Martin Kohn, that bear of a man, along because he was both a good doctor and inordinately sure of his loud, bom-bastic French, was amiably relaxed. Dr. Craig Leman, surgeon and former combat Marine who had been wounded more than once in World War II, was clearly enjoying himself. The other doctor, Marion Wier, was as always so wrapped up in her work that nothing discomfitted her. She and our two nurses were in print cottons, already wilting in the gathering moist heat. Lovely blonde nurse-anesthetist Priscilla Strong was notable for her spiritual as well as her physical strength. Finally there was little nurse Lottie Reich, capable, flexible, and wiry. She was so set on going with us it was only by chance that I discovered that she had been on duty all of the night just ended. I tried to make her skip this trip but she would have none of that. Like her, pharmacist Charles Dickerson was wiry, reliable, and capable. It was a good "cast."

Ralph Bellamy was already so committed to HOPE that I knew he would and could play either part—star-and-narrator or active assistant. Fred Rheinstein, the director, was a temperamental fellow, but such a lover of the East that our patients liked him as much as we did, and Dexter Alley, his cameraman, was an expert technician and a level headed, peaceable asset in any operation. Also with us was journalist Relman Morin, known as Pat, winner of two Pulitzer Prize awards, wearing ancient chinos and a washed-out khaki shirt. He was a man of great heart who had lived in and reported the Orient for many, many years. It was important to make known HOPE's work, in the most dramatic terms possible, and we had the best possible men to do it for us. HOPE lived on public appeals, on response from the public, and if they did not know of us how could they respond? It was wonderful that these men were along.

Congratulating myself, I munched on what were said to be sandwiches provided by Dr. An before he waved us off the ground. Rice cakes folded around Lord knows what, they served as a substitute for breakfast.

The trip took less than an hour. Descending on Can Tho we pressed against windows to see our destination, an orderly and surprisingly extensive town. It had been French, was now officially South Vietnamese, but the Vietcong who had infiltrated to the very harbor of Saigon were ubiquitous here. They hadn't much English but their vocabulary included: Yankee, go home!

As the Dakota's wheels touched down in a routine landing we noted that our airstrip was the only one open. The others prickled with spikes to prevent surprise, unfriendly landings and there was a heavy guard around the field.

Here, as elsewhere, was the customary knot of officials, the elders of the province, including its military chief, the medical men who headed the General Hospital, and two interpreters. Speeches were exchanged, photographs taken—for release after we had gone. It was barely seven o'clock but already the day seemed old. Rain began to fall.

The colonel of the troops who held complete power over the province rode in our cavalcade of vehicles. We left the field at well above the legal speed limit. Preceding and following were armored cars loaded with Vietnamese soldiers with rifles and machine guns. The colonel had quartered us in his own residence, formerly the French governor's palace, on the outskirts of town.

This building of yellow stucco sat in a walled park. Behind its trees, even up in some of them, at the windows and in the formal backyard garden, were guards, teen-agers, mature only by virtue of their automatics.

We stopped just long enough for the nurses to change into uniform, Ralph to get into his becoming new shirt, and to leave our bags in the rooms we had been assigned, then drove to the hospital where all the inhabitants of Can Tho and the villages around about seemed to have gathered. The outpatient clinic was jammed but before we could get to it we deferred to the Vietnamese sense of ceremonial. At a table in a tranquil room we met with the senior physician and his staff, drank orange crush, and discussed the work of the day.

It began with a tour of the wards, crowded with pathetic patients. They were well cared for within the limits of the means available but these were boys without arms, without legs, without faces, with terrible foot and body wounds where wooden spikes, driven by the Vietcong into the earth beneath the water of the paddies, had impaled civilians and guards.

At the clinic Martie Kohn and I promptly set up a screening operation at two kitchen tables and Marion Wier began working with children in an adjoining room at another table. Craig Leman remained in the operating room and before nightfall had demonstrated three major procedures to a young surgeon who labored so ceaselessly he had not even had time to read up on new techniques.

The faces of the people who came to be examined, taking their turns politely, said: Thank you, American, even if you cannot help me. Thank you for coming. Thank you for caring. The old, the young, blind, lame, crippled, the tubercular whose hacking coughs made it practically unnecessary to put stethoscope to chest, even walking lepers were there to see if we possessed some magic to help them.

A lovely Vietnamese, Miss Hoi, was by my side, interpreting, and Martie had another girl translating for him. Over and over they asked the same questions for us, never hurried, never impatient. Though we could not understand their words they communicated compassion in soothing tones. That morning I think we distributed more vitamins for less reason than ever before. The little packages were clutched to often ravaged chests. They could not heal, but they did comfort. The very old and the very young were the most touching and we arranged for some deformed children to be transferred to the ship in Saigon.

As noon neared, the patients, aware that time was running out, lost their stoicism and began to turn unruly, those outside trying to force a passage through the door. MPs did their best to control the straining masses. We went on working but it seemed that there must be rioting at any moment. Little Miss Hoi, who looked like a flower and was not much bigger than one, suddenly became a giant. She heaved her small self through the door and spoke in a voice that, within thirty seconds, stilled the angry roar.

We succeeded in examining several hundred patients that morning. How many hundreds were disappointed I do not know but the schedule had been set up for us and called for work in the hospital during the afternoon.

We had forgotten that we were also a "production"—not only a theatrical one, but an Oriental-hospitality one. We had flown into enemy country, traveled under guard, faced a horde of sick people and a near-riot. Now it was time for lunch and we were ushered firmly back to the palace to a vast table, sumptuously set, with waiters who mixed martinis and poured whiskey for us in an atmosphere of urbane sophistication.

This was interrupted by word from headquarters that the bodies of two of the colonel's men had been brought in. He departed hastily by jeep.

We and the other guests sat down to an eight-course meal with wine. The wine was for us. The Vietnamese know that Americans hesitate to drink their water.

Afterward at the hospital, we made rounds and held consultations until sundown. After sundown curfew settles over the city. We returned to find the guards had increased in number and we were politely but firmly ordered not to step outside once it was entirely dark.

At the final limits of exhaustion the men of the *Hope* and NBC and Pat of AP behaved like a bunch of GIs. We played poker, drank beer, and talked. When, very late, we trailed up to our rooms, it was to find a guard, cross-legged, with a cocked rifle on his knees, sleeping beside each bedroom door. No one dared tiptoe out to the bathroom all night long for fear of getting shot.

The soldiers at our doors got more sleep that night than we did. Again we pulled on our clothes while it was still dark, and the sun was barely over the horizon when we once more packed our gear into jeeps, half-tracks, and Land Rovers. The colonel, visibly nervous, snapped out orders, circling the vehicles attentively.

We were slated to go farther down the delta and hence deeper into enemy territory to Phung Hiep, which had seen no doctor, Vietnamese, Vietcong, or western for years.

Reports had come in, said the colonel, that the convoy would be attacked on the way. As acting governor of the province he, as well as we, was going where doctors were tempting targets for kidnapers. However, he felt our trip important enough to justify the risk. The size of the military group in the courtyard was a barometer of his uneasiness. Two hundred men, equipped with modern weapons, were ready to ride with us. Tanks, the colonel noted, had been sent ahead.

The colonel invited me, as director of our project, to ride with him in front of the convoy. Protocol, he explained. Top men first. But he pointed out it would be safer to choose a vehicle down the line, in case of a land mine, planted in the road during the night. . . . I rode with the colonel in his armored car, a crush of soldiers in the rear. What else could I do?

The driver tore down the road full speed ahead and damn the Vietcongs. Brush and trees had been cleared a good thirty yards back from either side to eliminate cover. Guards were drawn up to attention every hundred yards or so and at the rate we were going we passed two every ten seconds. Since night was barely over, outposts in village after village were still manned, as were gun platforms at each crossroads.

Though the road, a two-lane macadam highway, was good, all bridges had been destroyed and we crossed on makeshifts erected for our coming. In an hour we sighted Phung Hiep. With us arrived rain, rendering the day steamy and foreboding. The village was, like the others we had passed in the delta, compounded of crowded-together straw or palm-thatched houses interspersed with an occasional building of mud or clay, equally primitive, and two or three wooden dwellings. There was no plumbing or electricity.

Director Fred Rheinstein and cameraman Dexter Alley signaled us to stop and pulled out ahead to film our arrival. They went on and presently disappeared into the teeming rain.

However primitive, Phung Hiep was not to be outdone in ceremonial. The civil guard, boys no older than most American Boy Scouts, was lined up precisely. When we dismounted from our conveyances they snapped to attention. Along the path to the "hospital" entrance was a band of oddly assorted instruments, guitar and concertina, clarinet and percussion, the players earnestly intent on giving a rousing rendition of the Vietnamese National Anthem. Making our entrance into the clinic I thought: Very clever of Fred and Dexter to conceal themselves so skillfully that everyone behaves naturally.

Before us was the tumultuous sea of faces whose appeal

we never could withstand. Our mission as teachers forgotten, we went to work. Tables had been set up at the front of a large, unventilated room, an arrangement that had us performing as if we were on-stage. To one side we put up a cot, draping a sheet from the rafters to curtain it off, so we could make examinations of the most seriously ill in some privacy.

The pathology was unbelievable. One old man with cancer of the genitourinary tract hemorrhaged while he waited and went into shock in the middle of the crowd. I rushed to pick him up and put him to bed while tears streamed down his wife's face. No one, I thought, can say that life is cheap in Asia—to Asians.

We had been at it for about forty minutes when Fred Rheinstein stamped into the room roaring like a furious bull followed by Dexter with a sheepish smile on his face. Fred was swearing like a top sergeant. The idiot, illegitimate, asinine Commie driver, he railed, who was supposed to get into town before us, had barreled around a corner and the next thing he knew they were halfway out in the country again. His fury was three parts fright, I believe, the terror of being ambushed. The driver was likely as scared as Fred.

The tragedy, announced crescendo, was: No film of the grand entrance. He had been robbed of the climax of his entire documentary.

Fred addressed himself to the colonel when he got nothing but mumblings from us. The colonel understood no word of his diatribe. Towering over him, less by reason of his own height than because the colonel was a small man, Fred demanded a playback of the whole past hour for his camera. He didn't give a hoot in hell what was involved in getting everyone together again. It had to be done. To his mind if the mission wasn't on film it did not exist.

Across the street from the clinic a bridge had been blown up during the night and was even now being repaired. Here was the pathetic village, stating its own sad plight, the loyal Vietnamese striving to survive. Out to the mass of diseased humanity, Americans bringing help and love. And Fred had missed it all! What was the use of our work if he could not bring the story back to America?

The colonel, even if he could have understood, was profoundly disinterested. What was on *his* mind was that it was nearing noon and his nervousness was reaching an apogee. He began to insist that the time was ripe for us to leave. According to him he had a previous engagement, a celebration of the civil guard which he planned to address.

I explained that to return now was out of the question. We could not abandon all these anxious people. Impasse. Wonderful little Miss Hoi was our savior. She had understood Fred's intemperate English and knew exactly what the score was. The very gentle voice broke in on him. "Mr. Rheinstein,'" she said, "in half an hour we will do everything again for you. I will arrange with the colonel. Just be quiet and don't worry. It will be taken care of." Her tone was like a mother's to a fractious child and Fred was mollified.

At her bidding, right on schedule, the crowd outside rematerialized. We got obediently into the vehicles and, feeling a bit like fools, backed down the street and rolled up to the door again. The camera turned and the band played as earnestly as before while we tried to regain suitable expressions. The villagers, presumably, thought we had lost our minds, but they replayed their parts.

Shortly thereafter the colonel detached himself and some of his troops, leaving a lieutenant with orders to be back in Can Tho with us well before dark.

The more people we treated the more seemed to pour in, like tide up a beach. While Fred, in a corner, typed lines for Ralph to speak and kept barking for him to come learn them, our actor submerged himself in working as one of us. He carried children, helped the ambulatory, took temperatures—whatever was useful. When he did speak his lines it was with the genuine emotion of one who had taken, not "played," a part.

If we, plus the Viet army, hadn't insisted on Marion Wier's leaving, I think she would still be in Phung Hiep. She was literally inundated with sick children. One mother who came in the morning with a single child came back in the afternoon with her whole brood.

Night, like dawn, would come quickly without warning.

Before three o'clock the lieutenant who had been left in charge of our detail grew apprehensive. He and his troops preferred to obey his colonel's orders. We decided to leave around four, more than one hour later than we should have.

We waited in the street for Marion to finish her last examination, disturbed and rather irritable. Inside, the lady was all doctor. Ten, fifteen, twenty, thirty minutes passed, our tension mounting, before she was done. Then we scrambled into cars and took off at what felt like eighty miles an hour.

Night patrols were abroad, for indeed night soon overtook us. Pat Morin and I shared a car with Miss Hoi, who displayed no symptoms of alarm, shaming us by her calm. She talked quietly of how very much she wanted to go to the United States to study so that she could work with children in Saigon's physical rehabilitation center. As far as I was concerned she could do anything she decided to and I made a pledge that HOPE would make that dream true. The pledge has been honored. She is doing a brilliant job at the Mayo Clinic.

We were in grave danger all the way back. My heart pounded and my mouth was dry. Actually no mine exploded under our wheels, no one lobbed a grenade or took a pot shot at us, but it required all our nervous heroism to survive the trip. Our Vietnamese drivers dared the devil with their speed.

It wasn't anything we could boast about later and we felt deflated when we arrived back at the colonel's palace. There, surrounded by armed guards, we ate a monumental dinner, which began with Chinese soup, went on to the webbed feet of duck, pigeon breasts, and dozens of steaming side dishes. After that we Americans played poker again and talked until we were out on our feet. Those two days seemed like a week.

As the old Dakota nosed up through the dawn clouds that hung over Can Tho, I looked down on the torn country and wondered, not for the first time, how much good we had done. I don't know. How many friends had we made? Almost everyone we met had become our friends. Had we left hope behind us? I think so. I do indeed. The Vietnamese knew that the war would be lost if America did not help them. They knew that we were helping. But in the remote Can Tho region, they had not known and seen, till then, people from across the sea carrying mercy in their hands.

Chapter XXIV

On July 4 a round of musketry fire from a village across the river hit the SS *Hope*. The bullets barely nicked her plates, and the attack was more flattering than anything else. So also was the story circulated by the Communists that we cut off patients' heads and grafted them on each other's bodies. Such desperate attempts to harm us were proof of our growing popularity.

After the first two days in Saigon Harbor we functioned efficiently and what problems we had weren't visible. In the beginning we had a ridiculous ratio of thirty doctors, doubling and tripling in the available cabins, to twenty-two American nurses. As the Vietnamese trainees came aboard, clattering from ward to ward on wooden-soled sandals, the situation balanced out. *Hope*'s three operating rooms were busy from 7:30 A.M. until late in the afternoon and the wards were full, although most of our work went on in the city's hospitals.

The *Hope* was tied up at the dock in Saigon for two and a half months, at the foot of Tu Do Avenue which ran down to the waterfront esplanade, making us part of the city. Through the military cordon, put up to guard us, 9,000 visitors came to call in the first four weeks.

Among them were not only Premier Diem and the American Ambassador and the Vietnam Ministers of Health and Finance and the forty members of parliament, but all kinds and conditions of people. There were Americans from the U.S. Military Advisory Group and the American Operations Mission; Saigonese businessmen and professional men; prominent refugees from Hanoi in the North. Fifty saffron-robed Buddhist monks arrived from the far edge of Vietnam, almost at the Cambodian border. Shuffling along corridors in their bare feet, they followed a group of visiting nurses from one of the Saigon hospitals, who were just behind a family from Ohio.

There were few days when unofficial Americans didn't turn up to see what American dollars and American people were up to. A tourist agency referred to the hotel where its American guests would stay as "located just across from the *Hope.*" One elderly lady there said, "I watched the *Hope* sail from San Francisco. Imagine the thrill of seeing it here now from my window." Another remarked. "I have a personal stake in this Project. Last summer I sent $5.00. Now I've watched my money at work, I'll give more." Most of them wrote checks before they left the ship.

Hopies were also free to visit the city in their off hours and loved it. Saigon seemed to justify its self-bestowed title as the "Paris of the Orient." Vietnamese doctors invited our people to the suburbs, once the almost exclusive property of the French, where many of them lived in beautiful modern houses, elegantly furnished and surrounded by walled gardens. The colonial French were being replaced by an upper-class Vietnamese society.

Occasionally they gave big parties for us. One was a dinner dance at La Hippique, a private riding club, where jazz bands played rock and roll, Dixieland, *le jazz hot*—and young Viets "danced American" in classical robes.

As always our girls sang for their suppers. Johana Vettoretti and Nancy Campion were our soloists. I remembered back in Djakarta, at the Minister of Health's reception, when our hosts asked us what we would "do." Nancy told me that in Waterbury she sang with the Knights of Lithuania, the only Irish Knight they ever had, and I commandeered her services. She hadn't performed yet on shipboard and her friends glanced nervously at each other when she stood up. The first notes of "Oh, What a Beautiful Mornin' . . ." made them smile with pride in her. Then she asked them all to join her in chorus and it was thrilling to hear them singing so far from home.

After that Nan and Johana sang everywhere. Once in the outer islands, it was so noisy Nan couldn't be heard and Joanne Hefelfinger said, "Why don't you wait for silence like Marion Anderson?"

Nan giggled. "If I waited for silence I'd get a *djeruk* (grapefruit) shied at me." In Saigon she said happily, "Well, I've played the Palace in Sumbawa and they hung from the rafters. I've played the governors' parties and the rajahs' parties, the whole circuit, and now I'm a turn for Café Society in Vietnam."

It was a temptation to us all, especially for those who had been many months aboard, to eat on shore. Across from the ship was the Majestic Hotel with a handsome dining room and three blocks away the tallest building in Saigon, the Caravelle, twelve stories high, with a dining terrace on the roof from which you could look out across the flat, marshy delta. The river seemed to have no banks. Gray water and gray earth met and stretched toward the far sky. The safest places to eat were the Caravelle, the Bachelor Officers Quarters, and the American Club, but all water, and therefore most food, was contaminated. Some staffers who had survived Indonesia without a single bellyache went down with dysentery. In fact the only complete exception seemed to be Dottie Aeschliman who had grown up in the East and had a built-in immunity.

Shopping was even more irresistible. Tu Do Avenue presented a double row of temptations. There was no barter. Everyone in Saigon wanted Money. We couldn't exchange our dollars for piastres on the black market—which our Embassy was trying to stamp out—but even at legal rates, about triple black market rates, bargains were everywhere. A quarter of the asking price was the rule of thumb. Most of our nurses had signed up on the theory that they would not be paid at all, so even their miniscule wages made them feel rich. Here they could find shoemakers and dressmakers and endless souvenirs.

All of them fell for lovely Vietnamese costumes. One evening when they were asked to wear them to a party, though, they found themselves embarrassed. Beside the delicately boned Vietnamese, they said, they felt like elephants in fancy dress.

To me they looked perfectly grand as they strolled the city, pausing in outdoor cafés like the ones in Paris, except that it never gets that hot in Paris, or taking advantage of our honorary memberships in the Cercle Sportif, with its 200-foot pool and its tennis courts. You needed a swim after a day of humid heat that ranged between 92 and 102 degrees. If you walked a block you dripped, whether or not it happened to rain.

They looked more rested, too, in spite of the trying heat.
I suppose it was partly because they were so prettied up—
French hairdos and fresh clothes from Hong Kong and Saigon
shops and because they had had a vacation before the *Hope*
landed. Partly it was staying in one place and having time to
adjust to the strenuous situation. The quality they had, which
made them seem beautiful even when they were exhausted
and frayed, was not dimmed by comparative luxury, nor did
they work less hard. Dr. Herbert J. Bloom, a rotator who arrived in Saigon shortly after we docked there, wrote of them
to his wife back in the States:

> It's a memorable experience, working with the HOPE staff,
> and I have learned to laugh at situations that would set me on
> my ear at home.
> The nurses are the backbone of the Project, exemplifying
> the highest tradition of American nursing, here because they
> are great people with vision beyond their own comforts. They
> work long hours, have little social life, minimal pay, and live
> in far from ideal quarters. In ten months these women have
> been through some rough ordeals. Yet they are energetic and
> enthusiastic in their teaching of their Vietnamese counterparts
> and when HOPE leaves it may be that the greatest residual
> benefits will stem back to the nursing staff. In all the time
> HOPE has been afloat there has never been a single complaint
> about anything from a nurse. You should see them work—they
> really treat the patients with tender loving care. They discuss
> each order with the doctors and, when the orders are estab-
> lished, they are carried out to the finest detail.
> Each nurse has an eight-hour shift but comes on duty an
> hour early to check every patient with the nurse she is re-
> lieving. I would like to import the entire bunch back to
> Detroit but chief nurse O'Neil tells me there is not one on
> board who hasn't been offered a job by every rotator who
> has served with the *Hope*.
> The enclosed pin is for your charm bracelet. It's part of
> the nurse's uniform and Claire gave it to me for you. Wear it
> with pride!

Another American woman who wore the pin with pride was
Camille Grosso, a dark, trim registered nurse married to an
American Army officer who was stationed in Saigon. She volunteered as soon as she found us at the foot of Tu Do and
worked as a full-fledged Hopie for the duration. When we left,
she was still there to help carry on at the orthopedic rehabilitation center we had set up.

Volunteer Saigon Hopie number two was Mrs. Harold Price whose husband was employed with the South Vietnamese branch of ICA. Walking down the avenue she ran into Ralph Bellamy. "When two Americans meet halfway around the world," she said, "they don't wait for introductions. I asked him what he was doing in Saigon and he told me and he asked me what I was doing and I told him—nothing. He said they needed help on the *Hope* and strolled on." The next morning Mrs. Price reported and went to work as a secretary handling communications between ship and shore—8:30 to 5:00, five days a week.

The regular secretarial staff had a new set of problems. Where half the females in Moslem Indonesia were simply "Fatimah" and had to be tagged by ailments, the Vietnamese women all had three names apiece. Having no notion which we preferred, they changed every day, giving their names now as maiden, now as mother, and again as married. The rate of case histories "lost in the files" drove the girls out of their minds.

Before the stalwart Johana could cope with this situation, she slipped a spinal disc lifting one of our ancient mammouth typewriters and was put in traction. Competent medical secretaries are hard to find anywhere and there wasn't one in Saigon.

Rotator F. Howard Westcott, internist specializing in allergies, was just in from the States. He had written us as soon as he heard of HOPE. His father had been a medical missionary and all his life he had dreamed of doing medical missionary work, but while his children were small, he could not leave New York. Unfortunately our ranks were filled when his application arrived. He agreed to stand by and had come at once when a vacancy did occur in Saigon. His wife planned to make a slow sight-seeing trip across the world and to meet him at the end of his stint. She had been, Dr. Westcott told us, an executive secretary, in advertising. Medical talk was her daily fare and he was sure she could handle our work. We sent a full-rate cable to Tenafly, New Jersey, saying, "Help. Please come."

Georgia Westcott managed, by an act of executive determination, to get on a plane for Saigon forty-eight hours later.

The customs shed at the airport was its usual madhouse, but HOPE accreditation got her through as if she were a ranking diplomat. The Westcotts stayed at the Majestic Hotel that first night, until we could arrange a double cabin for them, and at 7:30 the next morning Georgia boarded the *Hope*. By eight she was flying up the stairs to consult Johana bedded in her cabin on the top deck and had already solved the triple-name problem by listing every case under all three cognomens during the first interview. The files bulged, but they worked.

She also got help from more blessed volunteers, thanks to our end-of-the-street location. A dozen American wives came along, with typing skills and hands to spare. Some donated half-days, some forty-hour weeks, and others whatever time they had. An oil man's wife who lived at the Majestic said, "It was getting pretty lonely in that hotel room. How nice to be useful."

The sisters, cousins, aunts, and wives of our Vietnamese colleagues volunteered, too. They set up an office next to the administration office and offered us an interpreter service. All we had to do was pop a head in to settle matters of faulty communication, like the one when a Viet nurse had hysterics because a "lot of men were running around deck wearing orange brassières." Ann Crary called in a French-speaking lady to explain that it was lifeboat drill for the crew and that the brassières were life preservers.

All our rotating doctors found a staff at work and learned immediately to laugh at situations that would set them on their ears at home, and to deal with them. In devising, each one, his individual program, they used imagination and originality.

For instance, take anesthetist Dr. Vernon Rickard of Whittier, California. After eighteen hours in the air, he reported to Senior Staff Medical Officer Dick Elliott, asking, "What do I do out here?"

Dick gave him a list of hours when he was needed in HOPE operating rooms and said, "You plan the rest yourself with the Vietnamese."

Rickard did. He discovered only two local physicans well versed in his specialty, one at the Public Hospital where eight nurses were scheduled for training in the high art so important to all surgery. "I found that a lot of surgical problems here came from lack of adequate anesthesia. They've been kept back from important medical advances by this. I decided that if I could teach just a few to use chloroform safely, I'd have made a real contribution."

Daily he brought three special trainees onto the *Hope*—Miss Dao from the Public Hospital, Dr. Toan, an interne who wanted to specialize in anesthesia, and Mrs. Tram, a nurse who was the only anesthetist in a small district hospital.

"There was plenty of time to train them and chloroform's cheap and available and dependable. But then I found out there wasn't a single machine for vaporizing it in all Vietnam. No machine—no proper results. The Saigon doctors and I got together and they said if I could design such a machine, they'd find someone to make it. I drew up plans, working in all my spare time, and the doctors found two shops to produce machines. How's that for a program?"

HOPE epidemiologist Harold Decker arrived about the same time as Rickard. He started with the local health officials on two projects. One was a collection of 300 specimens of blood from people of various ages in different geographic areas. The samples would be sent to the U.S. and analyzed at the Communicable Disease Center in Atlanta, Georgia. That was a first step toward doing something about polio, encephalitis, hemorrhagic fevers, and parrot fever. Project Two was an investigation in depth of the causes and frequency of dysenteries in Thu Duc, ten kilometers north of Saigon. We couldn't do much traveling, but the Vietnamese Department of Health got Dr. Decker everywhere—by auto or by air.

After ward rounds, meetings, and discussions, Minnesota's Dr. Norman Hoover finally heard mention of an orthopedic hospital. It was inactive because it had no staff. Hoover found three air-conditioned rooms, fully equipped, and sixty beds. "Can't you help me organize it and get it into operation?" the doctor in charge of the Rehabilitation Center begged. "Then maybe we can get some interested organization to give us a hand and we can keep it going when you leave."

Authorities granted approval. Dr. Hoover arranged for the hospital to open as an extension of SS *Hope*, with food to come

ashore from the *Hope*'s kitchens. Seven HOPE doctors went
there every day and Claire managed the nursing staff. When
our red-headed O'Neil discovered a room set aside for nurses
to take siestas or tuck into during night watches, she was
outraged. It became a utility room, minus cots. Before we left,
the hospital was undeniably a success. Other U.S. doctors
would come to spend time there and check its progress, staff-
ing it jointly with the Vietnamese.

After we had been in Saigon a short while, one of our Vietnamese colleagues confessed why he had been so suspicious
of us in the beginning. "Many of the Americans here act like
a clan. Not all, of course, but many of them. They haven't
associated with us and we resent it. Our people avoid going
to the U.S. to study because those who have been there lived in
segregation, something that doesn't happen in France. Then
when we see Americans practicing segregation in our own
country, we feel pretty indignant. You from the *Hope* are
different."

Because of the "difference" friendship burgeoned and cooperation grew. Finding us tactful, the Vietnamese gradually
admitted to their shortcomings and confessed their eagerness
to learn American methods.

These had to be adapted to conditions almost beyond
American comprehension. It was not only the ratio of doctors
to patients—1 to 25,000 in Saigon, as high as 1 to 100,000 elsewhere. It was everything.

In some operating rooms, attendants stood by with a broom
to sweep rats, lizards, and even an occasional snake out through
the double doors. One of our surgeons had the toe of his rubber
boot nibbled through by a rat before the rat was broomed
away. Many hospital wards had no sheets on narrow beds a
foot apart, and the seldom washed pillowcases were saturated
with dried blood. Men, women and children were often piled
in together, sometimes two in a bed, fifteen or twenty of them
in rooms ten feet square. They might wait weeks before anyone took care of them and others lay merely awaiting certain
death. Where there were no bathrooms patients used open
sewers running outside the door.

Betty Ahern sent a nurse for a sponge at one hospital while

she demonstrated a blood transfusion. The girl returned with a green floor sponge. Often enough there were no nurses around at all.

As Dr. Herbert J. Bloom said, "You have to work like hell in the local hospitals because there are invariable complications. If the heat doesn't get you, the rats may. You simply cannot do brain surgery ashore, but I can hack off jaws in damn near any environment and with a can opener if necessary. I went through several horrible days when I was afraid to walk down the street because people came up to plead for help. They all have a brother, mother, sister, child—sick or dying— and look to Hope for hope. This is a country of survival of the fittest, and life appears to be dirt cheap—but make no mistake, their love for their families is no different from ours—and mothers react just like U.S. mothers. This is a *tremendous* project and I'm proud to be part of it. I decided simply, 'I will do what I can and when I can,' and all my life, hereafter, I will have the satisfaction that I really served a worthy cause. Someone on this earth was made better off because I lived in it."

Chapter XXV

Bloom is an oral surgeon. After Hope's Dr. Phil Fleuchaus left, he was the only one in Vietnam. "Spent the afternoon removing the jaw from a forty-nine-year-old woman," he wrote his wife, "and it was a tough job. These people are all anemic and they bleed like fury. Their clotting mechanism, for some reason, is nil, and our blood bank is empty. It's all in a day's work. You do not come out here to play tiddlywinks. Part of existing in this area is an endurance contest. . . .

"Took a jaw off a twelve-year-old boy for an osteo. The O.R. is a riot—you should see it—the surgeons wear rubber boots to the knee and rubber aprons. The instruments are few and crude, but the students are eager—we had about ten in the

O.R. room to see 'the great American surgeon' work. Tonight the dental faculty entertained us at Arc-en-Ciel restaurant—in Chinatown—tremendous Chinese population here. The menu would floor you—not to mention what else it could do. Started with shark's fin and crab, then bird's nest soup with the whole bird (feathers and all) and the nest in the soup, abalones, duck's feet—claws and all—and the rest was God knows what. You brace yourself before and after eating. Hope there aren't too many of these affairs. . . .

"Right now I have a cleft lip, cancer of jaw, massive sub-maxillary tumor, and a tremendous parotid tumor (the latter I will do with the general surgeon). These people have so many associated medical problems—such as TB or leprosy. . . . Tomorrow we are having the local DDSs again for movies aboard. There are only forty of them in Saigon. . . . Have not seen anything minor, but I remove at least three jaws a week. There is more surgery here than most oral surgeons do in ten years of practice."

This large, quiet, pipe-smoking man reacted deeply to every-thing he saw, swinging between horror and appreciation of the efforts Vietnamese were making under such conditions. All of his reactions were tempered by sympathy and undertsanding, for everything except Vietnamese food. ("One more plate of snake or pig's stomach and I'm through," he wrote. "My G.I. tract doesn't know what the hell's going on at my mouth and I'm ashamed to tell.") Every day he went ahead "not playing tiddlywinks," working in all the Saigon hospitals and going as far outside the city as he could manage.

When a Mrs. Colpron brought a ten-year-old boy in from Bien Hoa, twenty-five miles away, to see him, Bloom was curious. The lady looked like a Fifth Avenue model and had a Dutch accent. He discovered that she and her husband were from Montreal and that Colpron was the only doctor in the village of Bien Hoa. Taking Captain Gerber and Claire O'Neil with him, Bloom set off with her by jeep to visit.

The hospital was in a jungle clearing near rice fields. Made of cinder blocks, it had four wards averaging sixty bare cots with straw covers to each ward. Everything was clean and fresh-painted but there were no sheets or pillows.

With five brothers of the Order of St. John of God and his wife to help him, Dr. Colpron saw 150 patients a day, did the surgery, nursing care, medication, and lab work by daylight or oil lamp. Six A.M. to midnight seven days a week, he treated all comers. Leprosy, TB, typhoid, tetanus, yellow fever, malaria, beriberi, pellagra, snake and animal bites, abscesses of every description, came under the care of this recent graduate from medical school.

To make hardships harder, guerrilla warfare went on day and night in the vicinity. The government had sent a squad of soldiers to guard the hospital. No one paid much attention to the frequent sound of gunfire.

"Colpron needs help urgently," Bloom wrote home. "I hope some of the hospitals in Detroit can spare equipment they are not using. World Relief Organization will crate anything and send it by U.S. Air Force planes."

On another day Bloom went with six others to an orphanage thirty miles from Saigon. It was run by Madame Ngai, a woman of fifty-six. The orphanage had been in Hanoi, above the 17th parallel. When the Communists took over, she walked across the rugged Viet countryside trailed by 200 children under twelve. During the 600-mile trek toward Saigon, she lost seventy-five of the children, but acquired another hundred.

Here, in the South, she maintained the number of her charges at about 200 on a large farm. It was beautifully run and the orphanage grew all of its own food. The children, Bloom commented, were on the whole a healthy, happy, well-behaved lot who sang and danced for their visitors. Ten of the Hanoi youngsters were in professional schools and those who had graduated were useful citizens. As her orphans grew up, Madame Ngai took in new under-twelve-year-old refugees from the North, whatever the nationality or breed—French, Indian, American, English, white, Negro, brown, and yellow.

The orphans were better off than the villagers in their bamboo-and-coconut-leaf houses, where the diet gave Dr. Bloom's puzzled G.I. tract additional reason for complaint. He had dog meat for lunch. Dog was eaten, even in Saigon, and the "puppy market" flourished just down the street from the Hope, but in the villages dog was a delicacy. "The poor eat everything that moves. All insects are caught, including roaches, and eaten alive. Rats and mice they dip in warm water, held by the tail. The idea is to cook the vermin but actually all that happens is they are drowned. The skin is then stripped off and the carcass, including the head, consumed. Village populations are infested with parasites from the diet and the people die like the rats they consume."

When a villager was bitten by one of the abounding snakes, from fifteen-foot cobras to fifteen-inch deadly grass snakes, he tried to kill it for two reasons. If he could bring in the head to a doctor, its venom type might be determined and the bite treated accordingly. Second, the body was food.

"Our country," said Dr. Bloom, "regarded as the land of plenty the world over, had better take some definitive action in defense of these people. Fast. Or South Vietnam is not going to be here much longer."

He felt that too much foreign aid in the form of money fell into the hands of the few so that the poor never got the benefit. The Vietnamese needed educators to teach them how to make the most out of what they had and a substantial number of well-armed troops to give them security.

"Come on down and watch the orderlies bring in small children from the villages mutilated and burned beyond recognition by night raiders, and let's see how you feel," ran an outpouring in one of his letters. "Fighting such opposition is no small task: the terrain is rugged, climate hot and wet, disease plentiful, and the local people do not know who their enemies are—perhaps the next-door neighbor, perhaps a member of his own family."

Thousands of people found their way in from the villages to ask HOPE for help, although they did so in mortal terror. Not only were they hunted on the move, but patients were later beaten and killed because they had received American aid. Still they came.

Dr. Smith, a wonderful American, was the only medical person within several hundred miles in backwater country around Kontum near the 17th parallel. Some of the natives— the Montagnards, or mountain people—were so primitive they did not wear clothes. When one of Dr. Smith's small patients developed a malignant noma of the face, horrible and common, her respiration ceased. Dr. Smith did a tracheotomy by candlelight on the dirt floor of a clay-and-thatch hut and then traveled through the jungle on foot, horseback, and by boat with the child and its mother because she knew the *Hope* was in Saigon, 300 miles away.

How she brought the little girl in alive was beyond Bloom's comprehension. The area they had come through was infested with wild animals, including man-killing tigers, and bristling with Vietcong guerrillas. Alive the baby was, but barely, her weight that of her bones. Half her face was destroyed and her lower jaw hung outside. Beside the child, her mother sat day and night, without sleep.

Bloom and Marion Wier refused to allow the baby to die when so much gallant effort had gone into saving her. Dr. Smith left immediately because "the people up North need me" and Marion literally breathed life into the child until Bloom could operate on board the *Hope*. Eight days later Dr. Bloom wrote to his wife, "The little girl is doing fine and we are sending her home in the next few days."

To save that child's life was an act of faith, love, skill—and time. The Vietnamese surgeons had to compensate for their small numbers with speed. If you took more than fifteen to twenty minutes for *any* operation, they thought you were "wasting time." They did total gastrectomies in the time it took our people to anesthetize and drape a patient. One of Bloom's Vietnamese partners watched him resect a mandible. It took two hours. "Beautiful," said Viet Dr. Dan, "but I have to operate on eight to ten patients in that length of time."

"My one patient is doing well," reported Bloom. "I wonder how his eight or ten are doing. Well, there are too many patients and one may make it. They *are* fantastic with their hands and cut boldly and swiftly."

Centuries of culture and standards of professional practice can't change overnight, and Bloom was well aware of it. He was also convinced that whatever we did was good.

"These are very warm people," he wrote his wife, "and one cannot live among them without developing a feeling for them. They are shy and very grateful for the help we give them. I am enthused—as well as confused. The future remains to be seen."

Chapter XXVI

Whatever we left behind is part of that uncertain future. Before I try to assess the effect of Hope's short vigil at the foot of Tu Do, let me give an extreme and dramatic incident illustrating attitudes before we came and how they were modified.

Dr. S. F. Herrmann, from Tacoma, Washington, went to the town of Hue with Betty Ahern, Genevieve Ferreira, and Dr. Harold Decker. Our team was impressed with the hundred-year-old hospital there. Out of 1,200 beds, 750 had been renovated and the senior resident, Dr. Quyhn, hoped to make his institution a model for all Vietnam. The operating room was actually air conditioned, though the recovery room was cooled by nothing more than a fan. In spite of heat, overcrowding, and a lack of instruments, the enthusiastic and skillful hospital staff was proud of its achievements.

On his rounds with Quyhn, Herrmann spotted a little boy outdoors who was crying. The three-year-old, according to a resident, had an imperforate anus and an inguinal colostomy. Herrmann asked to examine him and found the child a perfect case for complete restoration. Ordering preparations made and the boy wrapped in towels and bandages, Herrmann planned to use this ideal example to show what modern surgery is capable of achieving.

That same day Herrmann lost his first case, a middle-aged man. "The difficulty," he reported with sad indignation, "is that the surgical staff simply abandoned the patient after the operation and no one was called when difficulties arose. I found my man expiring from a low blood volume without replacement. The nurses were trying to hold him down and introduce a needle into a vein, but it was too late. No doctor had been notified when the anesthetist, without reason, removed the needle with which we had given a transfusion during the operation. I began to worry about the little boy and got a promise that an intravenous catheter would be cut down for him and inserted before surgery."

It was too late to interfere when Herrmann discovered that anesthesia for the child had begun before the catheter was cut down and inserted. To watch the procedure nearly drove Herrmann out of his mind. During the hour and a half delay the boy repeatedly waked up and Herrmann was forced to manipulate and replace the large mass of intestines over and over again. When he finally made the incision, he found his judgment vindicated. It *was* an ideal case.

In spite of all the problems, the long duration and poor anesthesia, Herrmann rejoiced in the belief that the child would recover well. He thought he had impressed on everyone the kind and quality of post-operative care that were necessary and the reasons for leaving the intravenous catheter in place as well as the urethral catheter which he had stitched in.

Nonetheless they were both pulled out and the accident was not reported. Still the child held his own, though his fever raged. Herrmann resorted to strong measures and afterward was promised that a doctor was now on call. When he went back again, the boy was cyanotic. No doctor had seen him. For this fresh emergency, a suction machine to remove puss was finally put together and penicillin and streptomycin pumped into the small body—too late.

"This was a tragic case, but it did enable us finally to impress on them *all*—forcibly—that the system was at fault. They felt that I had done very nice surgery, but I told them the surgery was of no value whatever if they didn't see to it that the patient remained alive!"

At the final staff meeting in Hue, Genevieve Ferreira preached about operating room techniques and the care of instruments and Betty Ahern demanded more efficiency in the recovery room. All suggestions from the HOPE team were received without offense and Herrmann concluded that we had truly made one vital point, "that the doctor himself is responsible for the care of the patient. The trip, with its two harrowing, unnecessary deaths, had great teaching value," he said, and "our visit will bear fruit."

I also believe the whole visit will bear fruit, though as I write, the future of Vietnam remains very uncertain.

The war has not been won. Terror rides abroad in the countryside, as it did when we were there. The enemy makes no common cause against common enemies. Though they boast of medical programs of their own in the North; the Communists deliberately undermine all efforts to fight disease in the South. Not only those who came to the Americans for treatment were persecuted. When men went out from the Vietnam Malaria Eradication Center to spray the swamps, the Communists captured one of them and decapitated him, hanging his head from a tree.

If the war is eventually lost it will be a mortal blow to the free world in the Far East. It will be a blow from which we will be a long time recovering. Yet no matter what happens, the *Hope* left a legacy which will last as long as those now living last. No situation or propaganda can turn our friends away from us, our thousands of friends. They will not forget the *Hope* nor the Americans who came with her and who gave without asking any return. As we pray for the future, we can look back with pride and truly say that we accomplished many things that did not end with our departure.

Perhaps the most important one was a basic change in attitude. Just as we had broken down the barriers between nationalities and races while Vietnamese and Americans worked together against disease and death, so we had broken them down between their own doctors, interns, and nurses. Hierarchies and compartmentalization can frustrate healing unless there is communication and an overlapping of responsibility. As we carried out programs in eighteen different specialties, we taught as well that no part of medicine is separate. It is a lesson all medical men, including ours, need to learn and relearn. The most brilliant operation is useless unless the follow-up care is equally expert.

I don't mean everything changed in two and a half months, but you could see the effects in the clinics, six civilian hospitals, and the military hospital where we worked, as well as in Hue.

We knew that we had sown many seeds and that they would bear fruit. Tact was the *Hope*'s password. Every man of us balanced any criticism with well-deserved compliments for what these men accomplished under conditions that would be a long time in changing.

Sometimes the good we did was the result of happy accident rather than planning. In Saigon, Vermont's Dr. Morrow performed microsurgery of the ear for a group of Vietnamese specialists. After this dramatic procedure, he had an ordinary tonsillectomy to do and was flattered when these top doctors stayed on to watch. Interestingly enough, their enthusiasm for the way he removed tonsils was even greater than it had been over the microsurgery. Morrow's heart leapt. If he had offered to demonstrate a tonsillectomy to such men their feelings would have been hurt. With the other operation as an entrée they could look on without losing face and see how much routine techniques had improved. Morrow suggested that we make a practice of introducing the routine by way of the spectacular and many other doctors slyly followed this example.

Whatever the Vietnamese learned from him, Morrow felt truly that he had learned as much. "They taught me lessons in compassion." He went with his Viet colleagues who gave their free Sundays to practice in a refugee village outside of Saigon. Asked to check their patients, he advised, in one case, ointment for a minor infection. "That will be good," said the Vietnamese, "but please give him a shot also."

"What kind?" asked Morrow.

"It does not matter. What these displaced people need more than medicine is the assurance that somebody cares about them. A needle is more expressive than an ointment."

This same friend took Morrow to meet the chief priest in a Buddhist temple. The priest wanted to thank us somehow for all we had done for his people. He was so happy, he said, about the philosophy behind Hope. Living in total poverty, he had no appropriate gift to send, but he found some postcards with scenes of his country. He cleaned them up, apologizing for the writing on the back, and sent them to us.

We, too, apologized because we could not do more, but what we did do will be cherished as we cherish those postcards.

Among us, we saw nearly 11,000 patients and performed over 500 major operations. By Oriental reckoning, we had therefore benefited over 100,000 people directly, for who aids one aids his whole family.

Twenty-eight Vietnamese interns and residents spent the entire time with us. Weekly medical meetings, daily rounds and daily conferences in all eighteen specialties, and regular medical school routine were possible because we stayed at the one dock. Almost all who participated told us that it had been the most worthwhile thing they had ever done.

For the children, the all-important children, Vietnam's future citizens, we had completed the first mass inoculation program, protecting them from diphtheria, typhoid, tetanus, and pertussis. We left behind trained local teams and ample syringes with 40,000 disposable needles and 250,000 doses of vaccine.

Two thousand books were left for the local medical school library and 20 nurses who had rotated through the *Hope* promised never to forget what they had learned.

We had opened the Orthopedic Rehabilitation Center with equipment from the *Hope,* including bed linen, and would help maintain the training program there while the Vietnamese carried on with our assistance.

We had literally introduced oral surgery to the country and Bloom left behind him a program which is part of Project HOPE and which we will help maintain as long as we can. After the *Hope's* stay a building was planned by the Vietnam government for oral surgery and the curricula at the Saigon University and the dental school were changed to bring them up-to-date. An all-out attack on dental charlatans was opened in the newspapers and a study was initiated to show why cancer so often followed simple tooth extractions in Saigon. Dr. Bloom and Dr. Fleuchaus were invited, more than cordially, to return to Vietnam, and two Vietnamese doctors, Tho and Do-Nhu-Kim, were invited to the U.S. Months after we left, Dr. Do-Nhu-Kim wrote to Bloom in America:

> My very dear brother:
> I continue to arrange our oral surgery plan in order that I can see more soon in Saigon of my very dear great brother and in some time my very dear great sister in law. I would very much like to go to the U.S. in order to perfect my study and see my precious friends. But I can't leave my country in this situation. Maybe when the Communists are finished, I go and work beside you. We struggle now more and more for defending not only Vietnam but also USA and the free world.

> For this year I enter in the Central Committee of the Red
> Cross for helping more and more our people and I work in
> the City Hospital and my private clinic. When examining my
> patients I often remember my very sympathetic brother with
> his "Tres Bien" and "Open." On my desk I have always a
> picture of you and *Hope*. I think it is the great event in
> my life.

An event is not enough. Of course it is not enough. But we
did what we could do with what we had.

On August 18 we closed the Saigon City Hospital clinic.
That was a sad experience. "One that I'm not likely to forget,"
wrote Bloom, "and one that will keep me with Hope as long
as I'm welcome. There are thousands who just couldn't get
seen, and hundreds have been sitting in the clinic day after
day hoping their turn would come.

"When we made the announcement that Hope must leave
for the U.S. next week, I got the full measure of our impact.
The patients crowded around me and with tears begged for
help. They held children up to my face so that I might see
their deformities, filth, and afflictions. People clung to my arms
and held onto my clothes and followed me into the streets
when I left the building.

"I returned to the ship tired, frustrated, discouraged, and
very sad. For all we did, it wasn't enough. I hate to leave
these people. They need us desperately, and with conditions as
they are, we need them, too.

"Hope gnaws at you and becomes part of your life. When I
came out here in June I wasn't quite sure why. Now I know.
We have made a staggering contribution to this country, and
to ours."

They want us to come again. We want to come again. That,
too, lies in the uncertain future. For the present, we go on
elsewhere, to others who need us. We take with us the deep
satisfaction from Vietnam, as well as Indonesia, of hearing
an echo of the Athenian attitude come back to us. They know
we did what we did in the name of freedom. Just before
sailing date, a doctor from Cho Rai Hospital burst out in
broken English, "I wish to tell you that the Hope people are
the first Westerners I can remember who did not come here to
take something away from us. The *Hope* came to give something to us. Thank you."

Chapter XXVII

On August 25, 1961, a lady walked off the dock at the foot
of Tu Do Street and fell into the Saigon River. With her eyes
fixed on and her feet mechanically following the *Hope,* she
had not seen her danger. Two bystanders jumped in to fish
her out and others formed a chain to hoist her back onto the
pier. The last we saw of her she was streaming brackish water
and waving to the ship.

We were on our way home.

A miasma of fatigue hung like a tangible cloud over the
Hope. The crowds were gone, the hospital shut. Visitors like
the saffron-robed novitiate Buddhist priests who had rustled
down the deck, were back in their temples and homes. Operating schedules had been taken down. But a forlorn note was
still posted on the bulletin board of the Intensive Care unit.
It read. "Sorry. No blood tonight." Some Hopies wore brown
patches on their right arms as souvenirs of donations they,
like most of the American colony and even the Ambassador,
had recently added to the dwindling blood bank.

On beds in the wards the pillow that a lad named
Achmed had loved so much he used to stockpile eight, flank-
ing himself with them and caressing them, were undented by
human heads, smoothly impersonal. In the pediatrics room no
almond-eyed babies demanded coddling.

"It's like a morgue," one nurse said fretfully to another.
The sudden cessation of familiar routines acted not as a tonic
but as a depressant.

Around us were endless reminders of the past months. Pictures of coral atolls and Balinese shrines hung in corridors.
Red signs in Vietnamese like *Phong Mo,* which had replaced
Kamar Operasi after we left Indonesia, pointed the way to
operating rooms. *Cam Hut Thuoc,* previously *Djangan Mero-
kok,* cautioned that No Smoking was allowed.

Empty, the classroom looked enormous. It had seemed
much too small on the afternoon of May 30 when our Indo-

nesian complement were awarded diplomas and HOPE pins by
their American counterparts and American nurses were given
their own HOPE pins. Colonel Dr. Sharif Thajeb, Dr. Bagiastra,
Dr. Beaubien, Dr. Elliott, and Miss O'Neil had made speeches.
Claire closed by saying: "You know, in America we have a
saying 'home is where the heart is.' Since we are leaving a part
of our hearts here—with you—in Indonesia, it will always be
our beloved other home."

In their left hands nine student nurse-teachers clutched
special certificates, written out in the best Spencerian script we
could muster and decorated by Genevieve Ferreira. In their
right hands they had Kleenex. It was a tearful time.

Three months later it had been the turn of the Vietnamese.
Each medical student received, as well as a document attest-
ing the completion of his course, a twenty-six-book medical
library. Many of them wept unabashedly.

We had parted with firm promises to write, and hopes to
meet again. In the months that followed some, like little Miss
Hoi, came to the United States and friendships were renewed.
Others wrote and still write. "My very dear great brother . . ."
"I am lonely and have no other occupation than thinking of
you." "War is growing. But I believe we are no longer alone."
"I pray always that everything shall be well with your family
and 'our' free world." "I know in your last letter that you are a
happy father: you can offer to your children a sufficient present
and a future. I don't think that I'm so kind to my two little
children. . . ." "When the *Hope* across so many seas, anchors
countries, coming to my one, a splendid horizon opens widely
for me. . . ."

Already we had a thousand tokens of our voyage. Orchids
plucked fresh from trees bloomed all over the ship. A joke
circulated about how customs officials probably knew what to
do about tubers but what were they going to say to a tumor?
The forty-eight-pound growth which had been removed from
the woman in Sumbawa Besar was such a medical rarity we
were carrying it home for other doctors to see.

Customs officials were disembodied intruders on Happy
Hours. The talk always got around to the ordeal ahead on the
San Francisco dock. During the ship's absence, the value of

what one could bring in free had been cut way down. Julie Wehrle worried about the silver-studded saddle she had bought in Ambon at the only department store she laid eyes on in Indonesia. When she tried it on for size, the clerks and all the other customers applauded. Her resistance was so undermined by this demonstration that she invested in a bridle, blanket, and stirrups, all dashing, all dutiable.

Peggy Donahue had a sailing ship made entirely of cloves, proving that she had visited the Spice Islands. The musical were importing whole gamelan orchestras, mandolins, drums, native xylophones. There were Balinese headdresses and packets of Far Eastern stamps for young brothers back home, a sacred totem, batik dresses and sarongs, lacquered and inlaid boxes, "clever" hats and shells from a dozen beaches. Bracelets jingled with gold and silver charms from Hong Kong and Saigon, Bangkok, and as far off as India where a few had snatched brief flying holidays. ("If I don't see the Taj Mahal now I never will.") There had been an epidemic craze for wood carvings, including models of dugout canoes. Also aboard was a dugout canoe, full size, belonging to Smitty, a steward.

It's a wonder the ship did not founder. Lloyd's of London divers had declared her hull seaworthy but she was listing again and working on the tilting decks was annoying and fatiguing. The Hopies took this new discomfort philosophically and prayed to God to spare them typhoons.

No one was quite sure the old girl could weather one. The angel who really does watch over the *Hope* sent quiet seas and for this mercy and many other blessings Father Magner offered a Mass of Thanksgiving on the afterdeck one sunny morning. The girls' voices soared sweetly over the Pacific from hearts filled with gratitude for the success of the mission.

"It's true, then," Claire noted, "that it is more blessed to give than to receive, although I must admit that in many ways we received more than we gave. We have lived among people who possess inner peace, who are not distracted by worry for the future. They respect authority without subservience. They are happy, lovable, and loving."

On the way out the Hopies had unpacked and inventoried. On the way back they packed and inventoried. This was a far heavier undertaking than simply making fast for a few days at sea. It was the ultimate signal that we were finished and it had to be done meticulously. After all, we owed an accounting of our stewardship to the United States Navy for one ship and to Americans who had equipped and financed the expedition for what had been on it.

Now, looking back, the Hopies missed the willing help of the camera crew. They missed the sense of adventure ahead that had sustained them on the way over. More than one began to worry about future employment when they got home.

America had come to seem so remote with mail reaching the ship erratically it was easy to believe they were forgotten. U.S. hospital superintendents interviewing HOPE nurses and technicians and secretaries might ask blankly: "The *Hope?* What's that?" the way the man in the Bowling Green office of the Merchant Marine had a year earlier when Nancy Campion applied for her papers.

For twenty days, while they took their hospital apart, they worried because their future was unsettled and uncertain but at least they could rehearse the recent past. They forgot the trials and the miseries and remembered most what they had accomplished.

Two of them were staying on. Marcella O'Connor was working in an American-run hospital far up the Vietnamese coast at Qang Nai for six months. Bob Toth, bespectacled, stocky, and studious, had fallen in love with Asia and was going back to the U.S. only to straighten things out before he returned for a year's work on Java.

The rest took pride in all they had left behind: medical personnel in Indonesia and Vietnam with brand-new HOPE standards; *dukuns* on outer islands who would no longer murder newborn infants with rusty scissors; students reading the thousands of medical books and journals we had given to their libraries; nurses who were inspired to fight for every single life and doctors who would no longer leave the nurses to cope when they could not cope. HOPE had been a teaching mission and to teach was to live forever.

It was also a healing mission and memories were vivid, especially of the children. The three small boys who were our mascots, who personified for us all the helpless youngsters:

Sana in Djakarta; Mala, the boy who was not only a case but a full-fledged Hopie who traveled and worked with us while his body was healing; Tu, Ralph Bellamy's protégé and ours in Saigon. There was the youngster who begged forgiveness for crying and the adolescent who kissed his nurse's hand and the girl who looked a little like Marilyn Monroe when she smiled for her doctor.

The *Hope* plowed through August into September. Sweaters and jackets were dragged from the bottom of suitcases where they had lain through months when the very thought of wool was distressing. HOPE uniforms, mostly worn to shreds, were laid aside. The rotating doctors who each in turn had played his own, self-designed part in the whole great venture were already back in the U.S. I was in Washington, working with directors, stateside staff, and loyal volunteers to raise money for a second voyage. Now the core and heart of Project HOPE, her ship's complement of medical personnel, her managers and her women, were coming home. Every one of them were invited to sail with *Hope* again when she sailed again, but none of them could wait idle for the months that it took. They had to earn their livings and many of them had to make up for what this time on half-pay had cost them.

On September 14, eight days less than a year after she sailed, the *Hope* came in under the Golden Gate Bridge, her pennants flying.

The cameraman who said HOPE nurses would be famous was right. Not one of them had less than a dozen offers from hospitals. Perforce they made their choices and, as did the doctors who had gone out for lesser periods of time, went back to work at home.

I tried to thank them, but there was no way to do that. I had worked for them and with them the whole year, but much of it from a distance so that the ship should have funds and the international and national agreements necessary for its operation. They had become a strong, intimate cadre, having shared among them much that I had missed. Sometimes I felt like a bogus rather than a *bagus,* a baw-goosay, Hopie. But, bless them with all my heart, they did what I could never have asked them to do, for love of HOPE.

Every one of them, spontaneously and without formal agreement, began to work for the future of HOPE. In their home towns and new hospitals, at meetings and parties and among their chums, they told HOPE's story. Over and over every time one of them spoke, checks, money orders, and cash came in to HOPE. You cannot buy friendship with money, but friendship and feeling can garner money for a cause so dear to the pleader's heart. No one who had served HOPE stopped serving HOPE.

That is the measure of its worth.

The ship went out bearing a simple message—*The American people wish you well.*

As Claire O'Neil said, all of them who were there left a part of their hearts in Indonesia and a part in Vietnam. Carrying the message, they had ceased to belong only to themselves or to the U.S. alone. Whoever took such a message added unto himself more than he gave.

Within months, the HOPE would sail again, this time to the countries south of us, first to Peru, then to Ecuador. Lessons were learned, the staff was to be increased. Organization was to be complete, efficiency at a peak. Only the spirit of HOPE was to be the same. Veterans from the Far Eastern trip who joined her again and fresh recruits alike would carry the same message, find the same response and the same rewards.

More and more countries had said, *Come, please come.*

Some day there will be a *Hope II* and eventually a Great White Fleet, ours and other nations'. Wherever these ships of mercy sail the words will echo as they did across the Pacific when we left Indonesia and Vietnam: *Thank you! Come again. Please come again.*

APPENDIX

List of Personnel

Stanley D. Abrams — Takoma Park, Maryland
Dorothy Aeschliman — Sacramento, California
Gloria Aguilera — Pueblo, Colorado
Elizabeth Ahern — Fond du Lac, Wisconsin
Thomas A. Angland, M.D. — Yakima, Washington
William P. Anna, Jr., Rev. — Beltsville, Maryland

Mark S. Beaubien, M.D. — Birmingham, Michigan
Renee Beauregard — Honolulu, Hawaii
A. Norton Benner, M.D. — San Mateo, California
R. Theodore Bergman, M.D. — Los Angeles, California
K. Irene Bernard — Chevy Chase, Maryland
Herbert J. Bloom, D.D.S. — Detroit, Michigan
Henry Bodner, M.D. — Van Nuys, California
Leon M. Bowen — Charlottesville, Virginia
Lois Boyce — San Francisco, California
Dorothy Burchett — Green Castle, Missouri

Teresa Mary Campbell — San Francisco, California
Ann T. Campion — Waterbury, Connecticut
Ruth I. Chaffin — Los Altos, California
Mark B. Coventry, M.D. — Rochester, Minnesota
Mary J. Crary — Ogden, Utah

Mary Jane Damuth — Utica, New York
R. V. Daut, M.D. — Davenport, Iowa
Harold A. Decker, M.D. — Columbus, Ohio
Robert L. Dennis, M.D. — San Jose, California
Charles Dickerson — Ann Arbor, Michigan
Maria N. Digges — Bradshaw, Maryland
Margaret M. Donahue — Grand Rapids, Michigan
Delia Dorame — Palo Alto, California
Merlyn C. Duerksen, M.D. — Covina, California
Davis G. Durham, M.D. — Wilmington, Delaware

Richard O. Elliott — Plymouth, Massachusetts
James Enright — Toronto, Canada

L. Virginia Fernbach — Floral Park, New York
Genevieve Ferreira — Oakland, California
Mary Ellen Finley — Los Angeles, California
Philip T. Fleuchaus, D.D.S. — Dayton Beach, Florida
Pauline Folcik — Flint, Michigan

William S. Folger, M.D.	San Francisco, California
H. Harvey Gass, M.D.	Detroit, Michigan
Susan B. Glocke	Berkeley, California
Mary A. Glover, M.D.	Kaneone, Hawaii
John L. Goble, M.D.	San Mateo, California
Joan H. Goble, M.D.	San Mateo, California
(Mrs. John L.)	
Bernard J. Goiney, M.D.	Seattle, Washington
John M. Gould, M.D.	San Mateo, California
Camille Grosso	Geneva, New York
Harry B. Hall, M.D.	Minneapolis, Minnesota
Elizabeth M. Hammond	San Francisco, California
Robert Hanan, M.D.	Phoenix, Arizona
Francis M. Harris	Garland, Texas
Walter M. Haynes, M.D.	Columbus, Ohio
Joanne Hefelfinger	Nevada City, California
Stanley Hellman, D.D.S.	San Francisco, California
S. F. Herrmann, M.D.	Tacoma, Washington
Max Hirschfelder, M.D.	Centralia, Illinois
Frank V. Hodges, M.D.	Saginaw, Michigan
Norman W. Hoover, M.D.	Rochester, Minnesota
Richard J. Ireton, M.D.	Dayton, Ohio
Hugh E. Jordan, M.D.	Whittier, California
Harriet J. Jordon	Woodside, California
Guy Kirkendall	Washington, D. C.
Edwin M. Knights, Jr., M.D.	Flint, Michigan
Ruth Currie Knights	Flint, Michigan
(Mrs. Edward M., Jr.)	
Martin M. Kohn, M.D.	San Bruno, California
Bernard M. Kramer, M.D.	San Francisco, California
Howard U. Kremer, M.D.	Philadelphia, Pennsylvania
Henry Kuharic, M.D.	Seattle, Washington
Mark A. R. Kuhn, M.D.	Fort Lauderdale, Florida
Herbert Lack, M.D.	Beverly Hills, California
Timothy F. Lally, M.D.	San Leandro, California
John F. LeCocq	Seattle, Washington
Craig Leman, M.D.	Corvallis, Oregon
James H. Lipsey, Jr., M.D.	Memphis, Tennessee
Stacy B. Lloyd III	Washington, D.C.
John F. Magner, S. J., Rev.	San Francisco, California
Richard S. Mark	Bethesda, Maryland
Stanley E. Mayall, M.D.	Spokane, Washington
Malcolm McCannel, M.D.	Minneapolis, Minnesota
D. P. McDonnell, M.D.	Whittier, California
Frederick M. McKinney	Marion, Illinois
Marjorie McQuillan	Seattle, Washington
Alexander Miller, M.D.	Cleveland Heights, Ohio
Leroy Misuraca, M.D.	Whittier, California
Rufus C. Morrow, M.D.	Burlington, Vermont
Dorothy Morrow, M.D.	Burlington, Vermont
(Mrs. Rufus C.)	
Florence Mudge	Escondido, California
Philip R. Myers, M.D.	San Mateo, California

Henry H. Nash, M.D.	Seattle, Washington
Richard M. Neal, Jr., M.D.	Portland, Oregon
Martha J. Nussbaum	Chattanooga, Tennessee
Anne O'Brien	Holyoke, Massachusetts
Marcella O'Connor	San Mateo, California
Claire E. O'Neil	Concord, New Hampshire
Mavis O. Pate	Tyler, Texas
Robert A. Peterson	Hollandale, Wisconsin
Eldon W. Phillips	East Alton, Illinois
Robert L. Pulliam, Jr., M.D.	Longview, Washington
John W. Ratcliffe, M.D.	San Mateo, California
Marianne Rawack	San Francisco, California
John C. Rawling, M.D.	Flint, Michigan
Lottie Reich	Glendale, Arizona
Marvin E. Revzin, D.D.S.	Detroit, Michigan
Vernon Rickard, M.D.	Whittier, California
Ralph Riffenburgh, M.D.	Pasadena, California
Dorothy Rivera	Lyons, New Jersey
Ann Roden	South Bend, Indiana
Charlotte Roller	Chicago, Illinois
Barbara Rousseau	West Haven, Connecticut
Alexander Sahagian-Edwards, M.D.	New York, New York
Nancy Savage	Lima, Ohio
Kenneth H. Seagrave, M.D.	Buffalo, New York
Harriet J. Siepel	San Francisco, California
Donald R. Simmons, M.D.	Detroit, Michigan
Arnold J. Smoller, M.D.	Mattapan, Massachusetts
Donald L. Snow, M.D.	Bethesda, Maryland
Paul E. Spangler, M.D.	Palo Alto, California
John I. Spreckelmyer	Chevy Chase, Maryland
Marylouise K. Streicher	Chicago, Illinois
Priscilla Strong	Pittsfield, Massachusetts
Irene E. Tegenkamp	Dayton, Ohio
Jack E. Tetirick, M.D.	Columbus, Ohio
Richard C. Thompson, M.D.	San Mateo, California
Paul W. Tisher, M.D.	New Britain, Connecticut
Robert J. Toth	Baltimore, Maryland
Johana O. Vettoretti	New York, New York
William B. Walsh, M.D.	Washington, D.C.
Gilbert A. Webb, M.D.	San Francisco, California
Julie Ann Wehrle	Hollidaysburg, Pennsylvania
Alex Weisskopf, M.D.	San Mateo, California
Hazel E. Wessel	Honolulu, Hawaii
F. Howard Westcott, M.D.	Tenafly, New Jersey
Georgia Westcott	Tenafly, New Jersey
(Mrs. F. Howard)	
Marion E. Wier, M.D.	Auburndale, Massachusetts
John E. Williams, M.D.	San Francisco, California
James E. Yates, M.D.	Stockton, California
James E. Youker, M.D.	Richmond, Virginia

*Former Members, Board of Directors, People-to-People
Health Foundation, Inc.*

Daniel W. Bell
Chairman of the Board
American Security & Trust
  Company

Francis Boyer
Chairman of the Board
Smith, Kline & French

Ernest R. Breech
Chairman of the Board
Trans World Airlines, Inc.

John T. Connor
President
Merck & Company, Inc.

Mrs. Preston Davie

Fred F. Florence *
Chairman, Executive Committee
Republic National Bank of Dallas

Elmer Hess, M.D.*

F. Kirk Johnson *
Chairman and Chief Executive
  Officer
Ambassador Oil Corporation

Eric Johnston *
President
Motion Picture Association of
  America

George Killion
President
American President Lines

L. F. McCollum
President
Continental Oil Company

Morehead Patterson *
Chairman of the Board
American Machine & Foundry
  Corporation

Industry and Hope Honor Roll

The following companies have generously contributed gifts-in-kind to
Project HOPE and through this impressive response by leaders in American
free enterprise have won new friends for the free world. Project HOPE is
grateful for their support. This list does not include companies that have
contributed financially or those that have specifically requested no listing.

Abbott Laboratories
Academic Press
Acousticon International
Adams Packing Company
Adolph's Ltd.
Advance Floor Machine Co.
Aeroplast Corporation
Air Reduction, Inc.
Air Shields, Inc.
Airkem, Inc.
Alaska Packers Association
Albers Milling Company
Alcon Laboratories, Inc.
Alconox, Inc.
Allan Brothers
Allergan Pharmaceuticals, Inc.
A. S. Aloe
Alpha Aromatics, Inc.

Ambco Electronics
Ambrosia Chocolate Company
American Association of Blood
  Banks
American Bakeries
American Can Corporation
American Cancer Society
American College of Radiology
American Cyanamid Company
American Cystoscope Makers, Inc.
American Dental Association
American Food Laboratories, Inc.
American Home Foods
American Home Products
American Hospital Association
American Hospital Supply
  Company
American Licorice Company

* Deceased

American Maize Products Company
American Manufacturer's Export
American Marine Paint Company
American Medical Association
American Merchant Marine
  Library
American National Red Cross
American Optical Company
American Pharmaceutical Company
American Radio Relay League
American Society of Hospital
  Pharcamists
American Speedlight Corporation
American Sponge and Chamois
  Company
American Sterilizer Company
American Tobacco Company
American Uniform Company
Ames Company, Inc.
A. Paul Amos Warehouse
Ampex-Audio, Inc.
Anchor Hocking Glass Co.
Anchor Products Company
Angelica Uniforms
Apple Growers Association
Appleton Century Crofts
Archer Taylor Drug Company
Ark-Home Farms Frozen Foods,
  Inc.
Armour Pharmaceutical Company
Arnar-Stone Laboratories, Inc.
Arno Company
Arthur Schmidt & Associates
Artichoke Industries, Inc.
Arzol Chemical Company
Astatic Corporation
Astra Pharmaceutical Products, Inc.
Atlantic Stamping Company
Awrey Bakeries, Inc.
Ayerst Laboratories, Inc.

Baltimore Biological Laboratory,
  Inc.
C. R. Bard, Inc.
Bard-Parker Company, Inc.
Barnes-Hind Laboratories, Inc.
W. A. Baum Company
Bausch and Lomb, Inc.
Baxter Laboratories, Inc.
Beacon Laboratories, Inc.
Beaulieu Vineyard
Beckman Instruments, Inc.
Becton, Dickinson & Company
Bell & Howell Foundation
Beltone Hearing Aid Company
Berivon Company
Best Foods
David Bilgore & Company, Inc.
Biochemical Procedures

Bird Corporation
The Birtcher Corporation
The Bishop & Babcock Electronics
  Co.
Blake, Moffitt & Towne Company
Bloch & Guggenheimer, Inc.
Blue Lake Packers, Inc.
Blue Ribbon Growers, Inc.
Blue Star Growers, Inc.
Blumenthal Brothers Candies, Inc.
Bolderman Chocolate Company
F. E. Booth Company, Inc.
Borden Foods Company
Bordo Products Company
Bowey's Inc.
Bristol Laboratories
Bristol-Meyers
Broemmel Pharmaceutical Co.
Brown & Williamson Company
Brunswick Corporation
Buffington Electronics, Inc.
Bumble Bee Seafoods Inc.
Burdick Equipment Company
Burnham & Morrill Company
Burroughs Wellcome & Company,
  Inc.
Burton & Parsons Company
Robert Busse & Company
Butterworth Inc.

Cadillac Gage Company
California Fish Canners Assn.
California Grape & Tree Fruit
  League
California & Hawaiian Sugar
  Refining Corp.
California Marine Curing &
  Packing Co.
California Packing Corporation
California Olive Assn.
Campbell Soup Company
Canada Dry
Candy, Chocolate, Confectionery
  Institute of America
Carnation Company
Cascadian Fruit Shippers
Cascoa Growers
Case Laboratories, Inc.
Cashmere Fruit Exchange
Cashmere Pioneer Growers
Cantaloupe Advisory Board
L. D. Caulk
Cetylite Industries
Chalet Suzanne Foods, Inc.
Chattanooga Medicine Company
Chattanooga Pharmacal
Chelsea Milling Co.
Chemway Corporation
Cherry Growers, Inc.

Cherry Products Sales Corp.
Chesebrough-Ponds, Inc.
Chloraseptic Company
Christian Brothers of California
Chun King Corporation
CIBA Pharmaceutical Company
Clarin Manufacturing Company
Clay-Adams, Inc.
Clinton Corn Processing Company
Clyde Kraut Company
Codman & Shurtleff, Inc.
Coffee Instants Inc.
Coleman Instruments, Inc.
Colgate-Palmolive Co.
College of American Pathologists
Columbia Fruit Packers, Inc.
Columbia River Packers Assn.
Columbia Valley Orchards
Columbian Rope Company
Comet Rice Mills
Commercial Solvents Corporation
Committee for the Handicapped
Concannon Vineyard
Congdon Orchards, Inc.
Congoleum-Nairn, Inc.
Consolidated Foods Corp.
Consolidated Laboratories, Inc.
Consolidated Midland Corporation
Contadina Foods
Continental Baking Company
Converters, Inc.
Co-operative Growers of Okanogan
Corbin Farnsworth, Inc.
Cornell-Dubilier Electric Corp.
Corning Glass Works
Cowiche Growers
Creamery Package Manufacturing
  Co.
Crescent Manufacturing Company
Crookes-Barnes Laboratories, Inc.
Cubberly Fruit Company
Curtis Publishing Company
Curtiss Candy Company
Custom Materials, Inc.
Cutter Laboratories

Dade Reagents, Inc.
Dairy Maid Products
Dairy Society International
Dairypak Butler, Inc.
Damrow Brothers Company
Data-Guide, Inc.
F. A. Davis Company
Davol Rubber Company
De Laval Separator Company
De Puy Manufacturing Co.
De Vilbiss Company
De Witt Lukens Company
Defiance Milk Co.

R. U. Delaphena and Co.
Deming and Gould Company
Dentist's Supply Co., of N. Y.
Desitin Chemical Company
Desoto Canning Company
Diamond National Corporation
Diamond Walnut Company
A. B. Dick Corporation
Dictaphone Corporation
Difco Laboratories, Inc.
Distillation Products Industries
Ditmar and Penn, Inc.
Dole Corporation
Dole Refrigerating Company
Dome Chemicals Inc.
Don Baxter, Inc.
Doughboy Industries
Drew Chemical Corporation
Duffy Mott Company
Duke Laboratories
Dundas & Foregger Anesthesia Co.
Dunham Bush, Inc.
Duo-Dens Products Inc.
Dupaco Inc.
E. I. du Pont de Nemours & Co.
Durkee Famous Foods
Duro Paper Bag Co.
Dymo Corporation

Eastman Kodak Company
Eastman Tag and Label Company
Edgett-Burnham Company
Edward Weck & Co., Inc.
Edwards Dental Supply
Electronic Industries, Inc.
Electronic Teaching Laboratories
E-Mac Dairy Brush Company
J. H. Emerson Company
Empire Brush Co.
Englehard Hanovia Inc.
Enjay Chemical Company
Escalon Packers, Inc.
Eskimo Pie Corporation
Ethicon, Inc.
Eugene Fruit Growers Assn.
Everpure, Inc.
Ex-Cell-O Corporation

Fairview Packing Company
Fanny Farmer Company, Inc.
Farrall Instrument Company
Faultless Rubber Company
Felice & Perrelli Canning Co.
Fels & Company
Fenn Brothers, Inc.
Fiberboard Paper Products
Fisher Scientific Company
C. B. Fleet Company, Inc.
Flint-Eaton Company

Johnson Mat Company
Robert A. Johnston Co.
M. C. Jones Electronics
George F. Joseph Warehouse

Kaiser Aluminum & Chem. Corp.
Kansas City Assemblage Co.
Kelco Company
The Kent Company
Kerr Mfg. Company
Keystone Fruit Company
Kidde Mfg. Co., Inc.
Kimberly Clark
Knoll Pharmaceutical Company
Kohnstamm
Kornell Company
Kraft Foods, Inc.
Kramer Trenton Company
Kuttnauer Mfg. Co., Inc.

Lab-Tek Plastics Company
Ladish Company
Lake Chelan Fruit Growers
Lakeside Laboratories
Lambert & Feasley, Inc.
Lan-Lay, Inc.
Lanco Products Corp.
Lange Medical Publications
Larson Fruit Company
Lea & Febinger
Lea & Perrins, Inc.
Leavenworth Fruit & Cold Storage
Lederle Laboratories
Lehn & Fink Products Corp.
E. Leitz, Inc.
Leslie Salt Company
Lever Brothers Company
Libby McNeil & Libby
Liebel-Flarsheim, Inc.
Eli Lilly & Company
Lindsay Ripe Olive Company
Linde Company
Linesville Food Products
J. B. Lippincott Company
Lipshaw Mfg. Company
Little, Brown & Company
Littlefield, Adams & Company
Litton Industries
Litton Systems, Inc.
Lloyd Brothers, Inc.
Lloyd Garretson Fruit Company
Lord Mott Company, Inc.
Los Angeles Brush Mfg. Co.
Louisiana State Rice Milling Co.
Ludford Fruit Company

M. J. B. Company, Inc.
M & O Company

MacBick Company
Macmillan Company
Magnus Mabee & Reynard
Maico Electronics
Maine Sardine Council
Mallinckrodt Chemical Works
Mallory Battery Company
Maltbie Laboratories
Manson Growers Cooperative
Manteca Canning Company
Manton Gaulin Mfg. Company
Marine Foods, Inc.
Mario's Food Products
Marley Orchards
Marquetands, Inc.
C. W. Marwedel Company
Massengill Company
Maternity Center Assn.
Matheson, Coleman & Bell
Matson Fruit Company
Mavrakos Candy Co.
Mawer-Gulden-Annis, Inc.
Mayo Clinic
Maywood Packing Company
McCormick & Company
McCourt Label Company
W. W. McDonald Company
McGraw-Hill Book Co., Inc.
McKesson & Robbins Company
McNeil Laboratories
Mead Johnson & Company
Meals for Millions
Medco Electronics
Medical Equipment & Photo Corp.
Meirett, Inc.
Mennen Company
Merck & Company
Merck, Sharp & Dohme
Wm. S. Merrell Co.
Meyer-Blanke Company
James Millen Mfg. Co.
Mine Safety Appliance Co.
Minn. Mining & Mfg. Co.
Minute Maid Corp.
Minter Brothers Candy
Misdem-Frank Corp.
Mitchell Syrup
Mizzy, Inc.
Mobil Oil Company
Moore Business Forms, Inc.
Morgan & Sampson, Inc.
Morningstar-Paisley, Inc.
Morton Salt Company
C. V. Mosby Company
Motion Picture Assn. of America
J. Bird Moyer
V. Mueller & Company
Mutual Apple Growers, Inc.
Mynol Chemical Corp.

The Nakat Packing Corporation
The Nalge Company, Inc.
Nash Engineering Company
National Biscuit Company
National Canners Assn.
National Dairy Council
National League for Nursing, Inc.
National Soda Straw Company
Nestle Company, Inc.
Neville Chemical Company
New England Confectionary Co.
New England Fish Company
New Haven Rehabilitation Center
New York Bible Society
New York Port Authority
New York Tuberculosis & Health
Assn.
No Knot Hooks Company
Norcliff Laboratories
North American Pharmacal
North Pacific Canners & Packers,
Inc.
North Star Dairy
Northern Fruit Company
Northern Paper Mills
Northwest Canners & Freezers Assn.
Northwest Packing Company
Norwich Pharmacal Company
Noxema Chemical Company

O. R. Labs
Oberti Olive Company
Ohio Chemical & Surgical
Equipment Co.
Olympic Press
Ophthalmos, Inc.
Oral B Company
Oregon Fruit Products Company
Organon, Inc.
Ortho Pharmaceutical Corporation
Orthopedic Equipment Company
Orthopedic Frame Company
Osceola Fruit Distributors
Owens-Corning Fiberglas Corp.
Owens-Illinois Glass Company, Inc.
Owens-Illinois Libbey Division
Ox Fibre Brush Company, Inc.
Oxford University Press

Pacific American Fisheries, Inc.
Pacific Fruit & Produce Company
Pacific Olive Company
Pan American Airways
Pan Pacific Fisheries, Inc.
Paper Novelty Company
Paperlynen Company
Parke-Davis & Company
Paul F. Beich Company
Pearson Candy Company

S. B. Penick & Company
Penta Laboratories, Inc.
Perham Fruit Company
Pest Control Equipment Company
Peshastin Co-operative Growers
Peshastin Fruit Growers Assn.
Pet Milk
Charles Pfizer & Company, Inc.
Pharmaseal Labs
Phillips-Drucker, Inc.
Phillips Molasses Co.
Phillips Petroleum Company
Pianola Inc.
Picker X-Ray Company
Pillsbury Company
Pioneer Rubber Company
Pitman-Moore Company
Plantation Chocolate Co.
Plastikraft Corporation
Plough Inc.
Plymouth Citrus Products Co-op
Polaroid Corp.
Portland Canning Company, Inc.
Positive Identification Co.
Potlash Forest, Inc.
Pragel Portable Incubators, Inc.
Pratt Low Company
Precision Carton Company
Prentice Packing & Cord Storage
Prince Michigan Mfg. Co.
Pruefer, Inc.
M. D. Publications
Psychological Corporation
Pure Gold, Inc.
Purex Corporation

Quaker City Chocolate &
Confectionary
Quaker Export Packing Company
Quaker Oats

Railway Express Company
Ramsey Winch Company
Rayflex Exploration Company
The Reader's Digest
Red Stack Tow Boat Company
Reed & Carnrick Pharmaceuticals
Refined Syrups & Sugars
Reliance Dental Mfg.
Remington Rand International
Resiflex Laboratory, Inc.
Resinol Chemical Company
Revell, Inc.
Rexall Drug & Chemical Co.
Richards Mfg. Company
Richardson & Holland Inc.
Riker Laboratories, Inc.
Risser Orthopedic Research

Ritter Company, Inc.
The P. J. Ritter Company
A. H. Robbins Company, Inc.
John R. Robinson, Inc.
Roche Fruit Company
Rochester Products Company, Inc.
Rocky Mountain Metal Prod. Co.
Roehr Products Company
Rogers Brothers Company
Rogue River Packing Corporation
Rolando Lumber Company, Inc.
William H. Rorer, Inc.
Ross Laboratories
Rudman & Scofield Inc.
Rusch, Inc.
Ruson Labs., Inc.
Russell Stover Candies

Safeway Stores, Inc.
Salada Foods, Inc.
Samuel Smith Memorial Public
Library
San Francisco Bar Pilots Assn.
San Francisco Heart Assn.
San Francisco Port Authority
San Juan Fishing & Packing Co.
San Jose Canning Company
Sanborn Company
Sandoz Pharmaceuticals, Inc.
Santa Clara Packing Company
W. B. Saunders Company
Scavenger's Protective Assn.
Schafer Bakeries, Inc.
Schenley Industries, Inc.
R. P. Scherer Corporation
Schering Corporation
Schick X-Ray Company
Schukl & Company
Scientific Apparatus Maker's Assn.
Scientific Service Laboratories, Inc.
Frank Scholz X-Ray Corporation
G. D. Searle & Company
Sears, Roebuck & Company
Seneca Wire & Mfg. Co.
Shasta Beverages Company
Shearer Orchards
Shedd-Bartush Foods, Inc.
Sigma Chemical Company
Joe J. Simmons Company
J. R. Simplot Company
Sinclair Refining Company
Skookum Packer's Assn.
Allen V. Smith, Inc.
Smith Kline and French Labs
Smith & Underwood
Smith & Wesson, Inc.
J. M. Smucker Co.
Snake River Trout Company
Snively Groves, Inc.

M. L. Snyder & Son, Inc.
Soundscriber Corporation
Southern Fruit Distributors, Inc.
Sparta Brush Company
Spiegel Farms, Inc.
Springer Publishing Co.
Springfield Greene Industries, Inc.
E. R. Squibb & Sons
St. Regis Paper Company
Stadelman Fruit Company
A. E. Staley Mfg. Co.
Standard Vanilla Company
Stanislaus Food Products, Inc.
Star Dental Mfg. Co., Inc.
Star-Kist Foods, Inc.
Starr Foods, Inc.
Stayton Canning Company
Stein Hall & Company
Steiner Corporation
Sterilon Corporation
J. P. Stevens Company
Stokely-Van Camp, Inc.
Storz Instrument Company
Strand Fruit & Storage Co.
Strasenburgh Labs
Charles G. Summers, Jr., Inc.
Summit Laboratories
Sun Garden Packing Company
Sun Maid Raisin Co.
Sunkist Growers, Inc.
Surgident, Ltd.
Sutures, Inc.
Sweden Freezers Mfg. Co.
Swift Motion Picture Labs., Inc.

T. P. Labs
Taylor Instrument Company
Teaching Materials Corporation
Teca Corporation
Technicon
Teletype Corporation
Theatre Network Television, Inc.
Thermolyne Corporation
Thermopatch Corporation
Arthur H. Thomas Company
Charles C. Thomas Company
Thornley & Pitt Company
Thornton Canning Company
Tillie Lewis Foods, Inc.
Tonasket Wenoka Growers
Tonasket United Growers
Torrington Company
Todd Shipyards
J. C. Tracy & Company
Travenol Labs
TreeSweet Products Company
Tri-Ex Tower Corporation
Tri-Valley Packing Ass'n.
Tubbs Cordage Company

Turco Products, Inc.
Turlock Cooperative Growers

Umatilla Canning Company
Uncle Ben's, Inc.
Uni-Tech Chemical Manufacturing Co.
Union Carbide, Inc.
Union Sugar Company
United Fresh Fruit & Vegetable Assn.
United Instant Coffee Company
University Film Service
University of Iowa
University of Oklahoma
Upjohn Company
Urb Products Corporation
U. S. Borax & Chemical Corp.
U. S. Catheter & Instrument Corp.
U. S. Pumice Supply Company
U. S. Vitamin & Pharmaceutical Corp.

Van Camp Sea Food Company
Van Leer Chocolate Corporation
Van Waters & Rogers, Inc.
Vegetable Oil Products, Inc.
Vermont Rehabilitation Center
Viewlex, Inc.

W. T. S. Pharmaceuticals
Warner & Chilcott
Warner-Lambert Pharmaceutical Co.
Washington Apple Growers Ass'n.
Washington Fish & Oyster Co. of Calif.
Washington Fruit Growers
Washington Fruit & Produce Co.
Washington-Oregon-Idaho Foods
Waukesha Foundry Company
Welch-Allyn Company
Welch Apples, Inc.

James O. Welch Company
Wells & Wade Fruit Company
Wenatchee Beebe Orchard Company
Wenatchee Wenoka Growers Assn.
Wesson Oil & Snowdrift Sales Co.
Western Anaesthesia Equipment Co.
Western California Fish Canners
Westward Dental Products
Wexler Film Productions
Weyerhauser Company
Whip-Mix Corporation
White Candy Company
S. S. White Dental Mfg. Co.
White Mfg. Company
John Wiley & Sons, Inc.
Wilkes-Barre Kiwanis Wheel Chair Club
Will Corporation
Will Ross, Inc.
J. B. Williams Company
Williams Fruit Company
Williams Gold Refining Company
Williams & Wilkins Co.
Willys Motors, Inc.
Wilmot Castle Company
Charles S. Wilson Memorial Hospital
Winthrop Laboratories
The Witt Cornice Company
Woods Canning Company
F. G. Wool Packing Co.
Wright Manufacturing Co.
Wyeth Laboratories

Yakima Fruit & Cold Storage
Yakima Fruit Growers Ass'n.
Year Book Medical Publishers
Yellow Springs Instrument Co.

Zenith Radio Corp.
Zimmer Mfg. Co.